Everything your kids ever wanted to know about dinosaurs . . .

Everything your kids ever wanted to know about dinosaurs and you were afraid they'd ask

Teri Degler

A Birch Lane Press Book
Published by Carol Publishing Group

Contents

I would like to dedicate this book to Kristin Kobielski, Robert Kobielski, Ben Pond, and all the children who helped make the world of the dinosaurs real to me again.

Acknowledgements

I would like to express my great appreciation to the many people who helped with the creation of this book. The staff at the Tyrrell Museum of Palaeontology—including paleontologists Dr. Phil Currie and Dr. Paul Johnston, librarians Connie Hall and Lorna Johnson, and Maureen Johnston from the education department—were all particularly helpful. So too were many members of the staff at the Royal Ontario Museum, including Dr. Chris McGowan and Kevin Seymour from the vertebrate paleontology department and Alice Chrysler and David Kinsmen from the education department.

A special thanks also goes to teacher John Bertram from the East York Board of Education and his 1989/90 junior-level class from Bennington Heights School for helping me discover what kids really want to know about dinosaurs. Ralph Neth from Purdue University, who teaches a course on dinosaurs for gifted children and also operates the Dinosaur Factory, provided me with a great deal of information and inspiration. Jean Koveleski and other staff members at the S. Walter Stewart Library have also been a big help.

For several of the wonderful anecdotes that enliven this book, I would like to thank the guards at the Tyrrell Museum and the ROM, as well as Yvonne Kason, Colleen Isherwood, Deborah Schulde, Suzanne Sherkin, Judith Carter, Bob Payne, Karen Jovier, Carol D'Ambrumenil, and Adam Trumpour.

And I especially want to thank Kaz Kobielski—I couldn't have written this book without his continued love and support. His nephews Kristin and Robert were a big help too, providing me with the true dinosaur enthusiast's point of view—and continually amazing me with how much kids today know about the marvelous creatures that ruled the Mesozoic.

Introduction

If the amount kids today know about dinosaurs is amazing, the amount they don't know—and want us to tell them—is staggering.

What we—the parents and teachers of today—knew about dinosaurs when we were kids pales in comparison with what our children know. Combine this with the indisputable fact that most of us have forgotten much of what we once knew, and we find ourselves in an embarrassing situation—a situation that becomes downright humiliating when our kids keep asking questions about dinosaurs we can't answer and expecting us to know things we just don't know.

Whenever kids ask questions about dinosaurs, it means one of two things: they either desperately want to know the answer, or they want to trap you—they want to have a good chuckle over how much more they know about dinosaurs than you do. In either case, you'll be much better off if you know the answer.

So read this book. It's funny, but it's full of accurate information. And keep it handy anytime you are likely to run into a dinosaur—at birthday parties, on trips to the museum, and in the educational-toy section of your favorite department store, for instance. The truth is, there is hardly anyplace where you are really safe from dinosaurs these days. And where there are dinosaurs, there are questions about dinosaurs.

This book will help you be prepared. It covers almost all of the common questions kids ask about dinosaurs and, of course, provides you with the answers.

A great many of these answers contain information about size and weight. Since most Canadian adults are still more comfortable with pounds and inches than they are with kilos and centimeters, imperial measurements are given first, followed by their metric equivalents so the information can be given to kids in the form they are most familiar with.

Even after reading this book, you may still not be able to answer every question your kids ask about dinosaurs, but at least you'll be able to save face by saying, quickly, "I don't know, but did you know . . . ?"

Ask me an easy one!

Paleontology and the meaning of life

Right now, you may doubt that there is any connection between paleontology and the meaning of life, but you will soon discover that there is not one subject in the entire universe that is not somehow connected—at least in the mind of your little dinosaur devotee—to dinosaurs. Unless, of course, it's the one subject you happen to know something about.

Let's face it. We all want to look good in front of our kids. We're the big people, the grown-ups, the ones who know stuff—lots of stuff—the ones who always have the answer right on the tip of our tongues. And we are usually pretty successful at pulling this image off—that is, until our kids start asking questions about dinosaurs. Then, quite suddenly, it's prehistoric panic!

Your three year old knows the names of more dinosaurs than you've ever heard of—and she knows how to pronounce them. Words like Triassic and Jurassic are coming out of your four year old's mouth. Your five year old wants to know about continental drift in the Mesozoic—and he's not kidding! Your six year old doesn't want to hear about dinosaurs evolving from earlier reptiles—she already knows that. She wants to know the name of the specific reptilian group.

There's no doubt about it: Before your child gets through his dinosaur phase, you're going to have a bone to pick with paleontology. Questions about whether dinosaurs were warm-blooded or not will make your blood run cold. Questions about continental drift will make you feel like your world is falling apart. Questions about fossils will make you feel like a bonehead. Questions about extinction will make you consider your own. But don't despair. Extinction is not a viable alternative, but looking up the answers is. It's not cheating. Honest. Read on.

Q: How do *you* know, Daddy?

A: Sometime after you've read this book—probably right in the middle of the most brilliant explanation of dinosaur habits you have ever given, possibly the most brilliant in paleontological history—your enormously inquisitive child is going to say something like "How do you know?" or, worse, "How do *you* know?"

You probably have a good deal of ego-strength and this question will neither threaten nor offend you. But if it does, do not let your child know. Simply use it as an excuse to launch into a brief—and do keep it brief—explanation of how paleontologists can know anything at all about creatures that died out more than 62 million years before the first *Homo erectus* ever managed to stand on his own two feet.

If the truth be known, paleontologists are not absolutely sure about a heck of a lot. As Dr. Chris McGowan—one of North America's leading paleontologists and a veritable thorn-in-the-side of those who are overfond of speculation—points out: "You can't tell anything more from the bones of a dinosaur than you can tell from the bones of an animal living today." If, for instance, you found the bones of an elephant and had never seen or heard of one before, would you be able to tell that it had a five-foot-long (1.5 m) trunk? No, you wouldn't. It would also be very hard for you to guess exactly how much it weighed, how smart it was, what foods it preferred, or how it cared for its young.

You could, of course, guess. And that's what paleontologists do much of the time. They make well-educated guesses, certainly, but they are guessing nonetheless. They then take a large number of guesses, estimates, and

suppositions and put them—like the pieces of a gigantic jigsaw puzzle—together. The amount of reliable information they manage to come up with in this way is nothing short of astounding.

I can't help but think of a paleontologist as a sort of Sherlock Holmes who can pick up a bit of fossilized bone no bigger than an apple core and announce: "I can see from the angle at which this astragalus articulates to the tibia that this was a bipedal carnivore that could run up to 24.4 kilometers per hour. From the excessive wear at the top of the bone, I can tell that this particular carnivore used its back legs to karate-kick its victims in the belly. He also undoubtedly had a twenty-centimeter claw, which he used to rip out his enemies' innards. Marvelous fellow. Marvelous."

All silliness aside, paleontologists really are amazing when it comes to deducing information from the millennia-old clues they find buried in the earth. The sum total of these clues is known as the fossil record. And that brings us to the question of what's a fossil.

Q: When I die, will I be a fossil?

A: The tone you take when answering this question will depend a lot on whether you think your child *wants* to be a fossil or not. Either way, you're pretty safe because not all bones become fossils. Regardless, if you think the answer to the question "What's a fossil?" is "a bone," you're going to have to do some boning up yourself before you deal with this one.

The word fossil comes from the Latin *fossilis*, which

A good friend of mine worked for several years in the public relations department of a museum that has one of the finest dinosaur collections in the world. One day she was called to the main desk, where she found a man with three small children raging at the clerk.

"Sir," said my friend, "there seems to be a problem. Is there something I can help you with?"

"There sure is a problem. You people oughta be sued for false advertising!"

"Sir?"

"And for disappointing my kids, and making them cry. They're hysterical."

"What can I do to help?"

"There's not a thing you can do, missy. We drove a hundred miles to get here—and we came to see the dinosaurs!"

"Well, then, come with me and I'll take you on a personal tour of the dinosaurs."

"We've already seen your damn dinosaurs. That's the problem."

"The problem?"

"It sure is! Somebody should've told us they were DEAD!"

means, literally, dug up. At one time, anything that was dug out of the ground was called a fossil. When scientists use the word fossil now, they are talking about traces of an ancient plant or animal or its activities. Thus, fossils can include such things as eggs, footprints, skin impressions, and dung, as well as bones. Even fossilized stomach contents are sometimes found. All the traces of plants, animals, and activities that can be found make up what is called a fossil record for a particular time and place.

A number of things have to happen before fossilization can occur. The plant or animal—or the animal's footprints, droppings, eggs, etc.—must be covered with sediment before it decays or is destroyed. A complete dinosaur skeleton can only be found if the body was covered with sediment before the scavengers could get to it and scatter its bones. This kind of rapid burial is most likely to occur under water. In rivers, lakes, and seas, sand and silt constantly rain onto the bottom and cover whatever is lying there. Because of this, the fossil record for sea plants and animals is more complete than for those that lived on land. Sometimes, however, the bodies of dinosaurs ended up under water.

Not all fossilized dinosaurs were covered by sediment in water; some skeletons were preserved in sand dunes. They may have been covered quickly by a sandstorm or some other natural phenomenon. Over time, the bone—or whatever is being fossilized—is covered with layers of sediment. All the while, the organic matter in the bone, which is mostly collagen, is gradually decaying. As it decays, it leaves little holes and gaps in the bone's mineral structure—since this part of the bone is inorganic, it doesn't break down as rapidly. At the same time, water laden with minerals percolates down

When dinosaur skeletons are found complete, they are often in the same strange position. Their bodies and tails are laid out just as you would imagine, but their necks are twisted back so that their heads are located over their backs. It is thought that this curved-back position is caused by rigor mortis setting in and causing the neck muscles to contract. A skeleton laid out in the "death position" is strangely reminiscent of the ancient Chinese pictures of fire-breathing dragons.

through the layers of earth. Minerals—usually silica, calcite, or iron pyrites—carried in the water seep into the small spaces left in the bone. The bone is said to be fossilized when, after millions of years, all the original organic matter has been replaced by the new minerals.

Sometimes an entire object—not just the organic matter—has been replaced by the minerals percolating through the water and the object is said to be petrified rather than fossilized. In other cases, the entire object has dissolved away and left a natural mold. The mold is filled, over time, with minerals, forming what is known as a natural cast.

Fossils, petrified material, and casts are buried very deep in the earth. But changes in the earth's crust and erosion may bring them close to the surface again. Only then can paleontologists and amateur collectors find them.

Since fossilization has to begin to occur before a plant or animal has decayed or been destroyed, hard materials like bones and teeth have a much better chance of being fossilized than soft tissue. Recently, though, what appears to be fossilized dinosaur flesh was discovered, and this has caused great excitement in the scientific community.

Those fossils that consist not of the actual animal or plant itself but of evidence of its existence are called trace fossils. Trace fossils include things like gnawings, droppings, burrows, footprints, and trackways.

Paleontologists take all the clues they find in the fossil record and put them together to form a picture of a particular dinosaur and its lifestyle. Different clues help in different ways. For example, by putting the fossilized bones of a dinosaur back together, paleontologists can get a very good idea of what it looked like. Marks on the surface of the bone

One four year old has seriously hampered his mother's after-dinner clean-up routine ever since he received a kit with a "pattern" in it for making a dinosaur out of chicken bones. Now every time the family has chicken he carefully saves all the bones and makes his mother boil and prepare them according to the kit's instructions so that he can use them for dinosaurs.

If that weren't enough to drive her crazy, he has also added a new twist to the process. As soon as he has collected a few complete sets of chicken bones, he phones some of his friends and invites them over for a dinosaur dig. Before they arrive he carefully buries the bones in his sandbox. Then, when his friends arrive, he leads his little troop of preschool paleontologists off to the sandbox for the dig. Once they've found all the bones, they return to the kitchen, dump the filthy bones on the table, and begin to make dinosaurs.

As you can imagine, his mother really loves it . . .

Paleontologists know very little about the dinosaurs that lived in the early part of the Jurassic; much more is known about earlier and later dinosaurs. This is because almost all the early Jurassic rock formations ever found were from marine areas. What seem to be early Jurassic dinosaurs have been discovered recently in India, though, so we may soon know much more about dinosaurs that lived in those times.

tell them how certain muscles attached. From this, they can deduce much about the shape of the animal, how it stood, how it moved, and how it used its muscles. For instance, the way Tyrannosaurus rex's jaw muscles were attached tells scientists that he had a tremendously powerful bite.

Fossilized teeth tell a fairly accurate tale about what each particular dinosaur ate. For instance, the carnosaurs' daggerlike teeth—which, with their serrated edges, look suspiciously like steak knives—tell us that these creatures were, without a doubt, meat-eaters.

Fossilized footprints and trackways tell a great deal about dinosaur habits. A trail of gargantuan tracks near Glen Rose, Texas, provides a good example of this. The tracks record a long passage made by a herd of sauropods. Before such tracks were found, scientists had no way of knowing that dinosaurs travelled in herds; it was once assumed that dinosaurs were not capable of such advanced social behavior. The Glen Rose tracks also show that the adult sauropods travelled on the outside, keeping the young in the middle. This indicates, according to many paleontologists, that the sauropods were caring for, or at least protecting, their young.

Tracks made by an Apatosaurus in what was evidently once a river bed tell us that this sauropod knew how to swim. The tracks are of only the two front feet, so unless this Apatosaurus was performing handstands and other difficult balancing acts, he was floating along using his front legs to guide him. At one point in the trackway, one of his rear feet touched down lightly at an odd angle. Evidently, he used this foot to change the direction in which he was moving.

Paleontologists can tell much more from fossils and trace fossils. The way an ankle bone is attached, for instance, might give clues about how the dinosaur attacked his prey or how efficiently he could run. The length and width of a leg bone provides another clue to the dinosaur's running speed. Fossilized dung provides paleontologists with valuable information about what a dinosaur might have eaten and can give an indication of what the quality of his food was like.

By the way, fossilized dung is known as coprolite. It's a good word to be familiar with. If your child is becoming obsessed with the whole field of paleontology, you may hear it around the house sometime. In fact, if your child drops something on her foot and shouts—not the s-word—but "Oh coprolite!" you will know it's time to start saving money for her Ph.D.

Q: Hey, Mom, which came first, the Triassic or the Jurassic?

A: There's no help for it, if you're going to answer your kids' questions about dinosaurs, you're going to have to learn something about the Triassic, the Jurassic, and the Cretaceous. And if you think it's going to be years before your children ask you questions involving the geological periods, think again. A six year old asked me about the Triassic and Jurassic the other day. She knew the answer already. She was just trying to trap me.

So here's what you need to know about the geological history of the earth and how it relates to dinosaurs. I will make it as brief—and painless—as possible.

The Mesozoic Era—the time when dinosaurs ruled the earth—is divided into three periods. The first is the Triassic. It

I heard recently about a five year old who asked his mother to have a mural of dinosaurs painted on his bedroom wall for his birthday. She agreed.

The boy had told his mother very specifically that he wanted only Cretaceous dinosaurs on his walls, but since she didn't <u>really</u> know what Cretaceous meant, she assumed her five year old didn't either, so she didn't bother to mention it to the artist.

The painting was done while the boy was away from the house and "unveiled" with a great deal of hoopla when he returned. Imagine the mother's—and the artist's—chagrin when the mural was greeted not with squeals of glee but with cries of outrage and despair. The unwitting artist, you see, had filled the painting with well-known, well-loved dinosaurs like Stegosaurus and Apatosaurus, but—as the extremely indignant child informed her—these were <u>Jurassic</u> dinosaurs and were long dead by the time the Cretaceous rolled around. He wanted dinosaurs like Tyrannosaurus rex and Triceratops on his walls. <u>They</u> were Cretaceous dinosaurs. Any dummy, he informed his mother, ought to know that.

began some 225 million years ago and lasted about 35 million years. The second period, the Jurassic, began about 190 million years ago. The Cretaceous began about 135 million years ago and ended about 65 million years ago.

Very different dinosaurs lived in each of the three periods. The most well-known Triassic dinosaur is probably Plateosaurus. However, the earliest—and longest-lasting—dinosaurs were the coelurosaurs. One of the Triassic coelurosaurs was Procompsognathus. He is the great-grandaddy of Compsognathus, the dinosaur that is famous with your child for being no bigger than a chicken.

Jurassic dinosaurs included the beloved Apatosaurus, Brachiosaurus, Allosaurus, Stegosaurus, and Diplodocus, while Tyrannosaurus rex, Triceratops, and Hadrosaurus all flourished during the Cretaceous.

The end of the Cretaceous, of course, marked the end of the dinosaurs.

The next geological era is the present one. It is called the Cenozoic and is sometimes known as the Age of Mammals. Although it began some 65 million years ago, mankind has been around no more than 2 or 3 million years. *Homo erectus* probably came on the scene somewhere between 1.5 million and 300,000 years ago. And *Homo sapiens*—that's us, the "wise" humans—came into being even later than *Homo erectus*.

When you consider the fact that dinosaurs ruled the earth for about 160 million years, you realize that we have been around for a very short time indeed.

Q: Where is Gondwanaland and what is plate tectonics?

A: You probably don't know, and you probably don't care, but don't think for a minute that your preschool paleontologist doesn't. And she's going to want to know the answer to this and a whole raft of other questions about the world dinosaurs lived in. In order to answer them at all accurately, you're going to have to know something about the earth's land masses and the tremendous changes that occurred during the Mesozoic. First, though, if your child asks simply, "Where did the dinosaurs live?" you should try to get away with answering, succinctly, "everywhere." Dinosaur bones have been found on every continent on earth with the exception of Antarctica, and there's only one reason why Antarctica has been denied the fame and glory that the discovery of dinosaur bones invariably brings: no paleontologist in his or her right mind wants to go digging under all that ice to find them (not that anyone has ever accused paleontologists of being in their right minds, but that's an entirely different matter).

But the continents of the Mesozoic were very different from the continents of today, and your child is almost certain to begin asking pesky questions about things like continental drift and plate tectonics. In the not-unlikely event that this fate befalls you, here are a few facts you can bounce off your child's brain-heavy head:

Plate tectonics, simply put, is the idea that the continents are, in fact, relatively lightweight masses that sit on sheets of the earth's crust called tectonic plates. These plates, in turn,

At the beginning of the Mesozoic the moon was closer to the earth and would have appeared about one and a half times larger than it does now in the night sky. The earth was spinning more rapidly, too, and a day and a night were only about twenty-two hours and forty-five minutes long.

sort of float around on the earth's molten core.

Now, the idea that the terra firma beneath my feet isn't firm at all doesn't please me one bit. It probably doesn't please you either, but there's nothing we can do about it. Tectonic plates are now considered a genuine, bona fide scientific fact. And, to give credit where credit is due, this theory does explain why—as you probably noticed the first time you ever looked at a map—the earth's continents look like pieces of a gargantuan jigsaw puzzle that might have once fit snugly together.

The continents did, in fact, once fit together. Then they began to float, or drift, apart. This phenomenon is called—you guessed it—continental drift. The reason continental drift is important to the study of dinosaurs is that major changes in the shape of the continents occurred during the Mesozoic—the era when dinosaurs ruled the earth. At the beginning of the Triassic, all the continents on earth were lumped together in one gigantic mass called Pangaea (although who was around to call it that, I don't know). Thus, the types of dinosaurs that lived in the Triassic were able to spread all over the earth.

During the Jurassic, Pangaea began to split in two. The two new land masses came to be called Laurasia and Gondwanaland. (These names are for real. I did not make them up. But I wish I had. Especially Gondwanaland. It sounds like a place where a lot of bats lived.) Gondwanaland included South America, Africa, India, Australia, and Antarctica. Laurasia was made up of what is now North America, Europe, and Asia. The types of dinosaurs that originated after the split could not spread from Gond-wanaland to Laurasia or vice versa. However, they could spread all around their own great continent. Some types of

Although most scientists believe that by the late Cretaceous, the continents looked much the way they do today, the discovery of a dinosaur named Laplatasaurus in South America, India, Madagascar, and Nigeria makes some paleontologists suspect that a land bridge must have connected South America and Africa in those times.

dinosaurs, for example, lived in both Asia and North America; others lived in South America and India.

In the Cretaceous, the land masses became further divided by water. By the end of the Cretaceous, the continents were positioned much as they are today. The dinosaurs that originated after this split were segregated on their own continents. They could spread only to those continents that were connected by land.

The theory of continental drift is invaluable to paleontologists, and one day it will be invaluable to you. When your daughter asks, "How did Iguanodon's grandpa get from North America to England?", you will not have to embarrass yourself with quips like "I think he flew TWA" or "That guy could really swim, couldn't he?" Instead, you will be able to say, in a voice resonant with authority, "He walked."

In the late Cretaceous, a shallow sea split the North American continent down the middle. Named the Niobrara Sea, after the Niobrara River in Wyoming and Nebraska, it was a thousand miles (1,600 km) wide. The creatures that lived in this sea tended to be huge. The plesiosaurs grew up to forty-three feet (13 m) long, and some of the oysters were eighteen inches (46 cm) across!

Q: Could a dinosaur live in our backyard?

A: Probably not. The backyards of the Mesozoic looked very different from the backyards of today—and not just because dinosaurs didn't have barbecues, swimming pools, and swing sets, or because they could go outside without worrying about smog and sonic booms from Concordes and fighter planes overhead. No, the world of the Mesozoic was different because most of the plants and animals around today weren't around yet. For instance, when the first dinosaurs came on the scene in the late Triassic, there was no such thing as grass, a plant that colors the way much of the earth looks today.

Those early dinosaurs—like Plateosaurus and Procompsognathus—found a world covered in ferns and horsetails but with few trees. There were some conifers and yews. The cycads—those thick, stumpy trunks that have a few palm fronds sticking out the top—were beginning to flourish. The only mammals around were ugly little shrewlike creatures, but primitive crocodiles, tortoises, and frogs were doing well. Reptiles with winglike membranes glided through the air, and ichthyosaurs swam the seas. It's possible that there were widespread desert areas in the late Triassic, but nobody knows for sure.

Things were looking up for the dinosaurs—and a number of other creatures—by the middle of the Jurassic. The cycads were flourishing in moist areas. The early crocodiles, lizards, and tortoises were still doing well. There were more kinds of small mammals, some as big as cats. Early birds were taking their first leaps into the air. Large furry-bodied pterosaurs were gliding through the air, and plesiosaurs had joined the ichthyosaurs in the seas. Many of the most beloved of all dinosaurs lived in the Jurassic, including Apatosaurus, Diplodocus, Brachiosaurus, Stegosaurus, and Allosaurus.

Even greater changes occurred in the Cretaceous. Tyrannosaurus, Triceratops, and the duckbills roamed the earth. Some dinosaurs lived in the wetlands, others on the higher, drier plains. Some may have migrated to find food or better places to lay their eggs. The shifting of land masses created some seasonal changes and cooler winters, but the harsh winters of today were still unknown. Frogs, crocodiles, and lizards were still abundant, and they were joined by early snakes, soft-shelled turtles, and salamanders. There were primitive opossums and many birds, like gulls and waders.

The first discoveries of dinosaur fossils in Canada were made in the early 1870s, but the first really important one was made by Joseph Tyrrell in 1884 in the Red Deer River valley; it was the skull of an Albertosaurus.

Huge pterosaurs filled the skies. One, Quetzalcoatlus, was the largest flying creature ever known—his wings spanned up to forty feet (12 m).

There were forests of oak and hickory; there were swampy areas with giant sequoias, swamp cypresses, and China firs. And, in the Cretaceous, a great deal of beauty was added to the world: the first flowering plants appeared. Then, Triceratops could have munched magnolias—or sniffed wild roses in the cool Cretaceous dawn.

Q: Why did all the dinosaurs have to die?

A: This question has the double distinction of being the most often asked and the most difficult to answer. But the strangest thing about it is that I have never met a child—no matter how much he loved dinosaurs—that asked this question with a tear in his eye. After all, if the dinosaurs hadn't died out, they'd still be alive. And no matter how much a child enjoys having dinosaurs running around his imagination, he doesn't *really* want them running around his backyard.

A great many theories have been proposed to explain why dinosaurs died out at the end of the Mesozoic. One scientist, for example, proposed that during the late Cretaceous small mammals took up the habit of eating dinosaur eggs. Once all the eggs were eaten, there were no more dinosaurs. There are a number of fairly obvious gaps in the logic of this theory. David Norman, one of the world's leading paleontologists, points out a few of them in his book *The Illustrated Encyclopedia of Dinosaurs.* First, a sort of biological common sense present in nature keeps predators from wiping out their main food supply. Second, while it's just possible that a species or two of dinosaurs might have been destroyed by marauding egg-eaters, it's highly improbable that the entire dinosaur population would have been decimated. Finally, the theory does nothing to explain why so many other groups of plants and animals died out, including chalky plankton, ammonites, ichthyosaurs, plesiosaurs, and pterosaurs. Norman says that a great many theories on dinosaur extinction have this same failing. In fact, he says, once you throw out all the theories that explain only dinosaur extinction, you are left with only two viable possibilities: the cosmic explanation and the climatic explanation.

The idea that some cosmic influence—a meteorite, a rain of comets, or an exploding star—affected the earth and killed off the dinosaurs has been around for a very long time. In general, the most logical of these theories propose that the impact of some extraterrestrial body on the earth's crust caused tremendous atmospheric disturbances that, in turn, caused many plants and, eventually, animals to die. A huge cloud of dust, for example, could have blocked out the sun for a number of weeks. Without sun, plants would die off very rapidly—and so would the animals that needed them for food.

Until recently, there was very little geological or astrological evidence that such an explosion could have occurred. The cosmic theory got a big boost, however, when a scientist named Luis Alvarez was taking soil samples in Italy a few years ago and discovered a layer of iridium in late Cretaceous sediments. Iridium is an element that is concentrated, on earth, only in the molten core. One of the only explanations for this anomaly—or spike—of iridium is that it had some extraterrestrial source. For example, a huge meteorite might have hit the earth towards the end of the Cretaceous and caused a tremendous explosion. On impact with the earth's crust, the meteorite would have vaporized and caused a cloud of dust and steam to begin enveloping the earth. The dust, which contained iridium, would have filtered slowly to the earth and left the traces found by Alvarez.

If this is what happened, the iridium spike should be found in other parts of the world. Soon after Alvarez announced his discovery and proposed his theory, other scientists began to look for the iridium spike in a few other locations. Sure enough, they found it, but it is still not known whether the iridium spike will be found all around the world. It may be that the iridium deposits were left not by a meteorite but by heavy volcanic activity at the end of the Cretaceous.

Another currently popular cosmic explanation is that the earth is bombarded every 26 million years by a rain of comets. It is supposed that these comets are shaken by some cosmic force out of the Oort Cloud, a vast field of comets that is in orbit about nine million miles (15,000,000 km) from the sun.

There are several ideas about the exact nature of the cosmic force or event that would shake the comets out of the Oort Cloud. One supposes the existence of an as-yet-undiscovered tenth planet. This planet might have an unusual orbit that would take it through the field of comets only at intervals of about 26 million years. Another theory proposes that our sun is actually part of a binary star system—in other words, our sun has a companion star. This star could possibly have an extremely elliptical orbit—which would explain why

no one has seen it yet—that would bring it close enough to exert gravitational influence on the Oort Cloud about once every 26 million years.

One of the problems with all of the cosmic theories is that they don't offer a satisfactory explanation for why some animals and plants died and others lived.

Within the cosmic school of thought, each theory has its proponents and critics, who debate their ideas with extreme vigor. Proponents of the climatic change theory don't think any of the cosmic theories are right. A number of them believe that the mass extinction at the end of the Cretaceous occurred, not suddenly and dramatically, but slowly and gradually. After all, when we talk about the late Cretaceous, we are talking about a span in time of millions of years.

One group of scientists has made an extensive study of plant life during this time. They say that between 5 and 10 million years before the end of the Cretaceous, there was abundant, lush subtropical and tropical plant life. A wide variety of dinosaurs could—and did—survive on such plants. Towards the close of the period, however, the kinds of plants that thrive in cool, woodland areas became more abundant. The logical deduction to be made from the changes in plant life is that the world's climate was slowly deteriorating and that some of the tropical and subtropical areas were becoming cool and dry. It is interesting to note that fossil finds from this period indicate there were fewer types of dinosaurs living in that time. Also, the small mammals—who with their fur insulation would naturally thrive in the cooler woodlands—became much more numerous.

Continental drift provides a logical explanation for these climatic changes. By the late Cretaceous, the major continents

Baron Georges Cuvier (1769–1832) is known as the father of paleontology and comparative anatomy. He was one of the first to promote the idea that animals could become extinct.

Prior to Cuvier's work—and to the discovery of a huge Mosasaurus jaw in Holland in 1770, which provided Cuvier with strong evidence for his theories—it was believed that God had created all living things at the time of creation. It was considered unthinkable that God would let any of His creatures become extinct.

Fossils found before Cuvier's theories became generally accepted were believed to be the bones of dead animals that still populated the earth.

had separated. The spreading of the sea floor brought about by this separation would have caused sea levels to rise. This would have altered ocean currents and, in turn, wind patterns. The mild weather conditions that may have been typical in the Triassic and Jurassic could easily have been altered by such changes, and as a result, the late Cretaceous may have become cool and seasonal.

Like the cosmic theory, the climatic theory doesn't explain why some species survived and others didn't. Ultimately, some scientists find problems with both theories, and as is so often the case when science is dealing with something that happened millions upon millions of years ago, proof is very difficult to come by. However, the recent discovery of the iridium spike, the advances in astronomy, and a passionate renewal in the public's interest in dinosaurs have sparked a great deal of activity. Scientists from many disciplines are working around the world and amassing information that will help us understand why the reign of the dinosaurs ended.

It's exciting to think science might be on the brink of answering a question that has perplexed us from the moment we first realized that dinosaurs once lived.

Q: Were dinosaurs a failure?

A: No. Absolutely not.

Unfortunately, there is a pervasive misconception that dinosaurs were an unsuccessful evolutionary experiment who died out because their brains were too small and they were unable to adapt. It's time we took the Tyrannosaurus by the tail and did something about changing this belief. The first step should be to clean up our language. We must pledge to never again use the word dinosaur to refer to old-fashioned, unworkable ideas, huge, unused buildings that have fallen into disrepair, big, dilapidated pieces of machinery, or—especially—a person whose backward thinking is about to make him extinct.

Dinosaurs were, after all, a tremendously successful group of animals. They ruled the earth for the better part of 160 million years. That's an amazing stretch of time. The last dinosaurs actually lived closer in time to us than to the first dinosaurs!

The dinosaurs' phenomenal success seems even more amazing when you consider that a number of mammal-like reptiles and true mammals were also around in the Mesozoic. This astounds people who assume that as soon as mammals came on the scene they must have taken over—after all, *we're* mammals.

According to some paleontologists, dinosaurs had appeared by the middle of the first period of the Mesozoic, the Triassic, which began 225 million years ago. They didn't really come into their full glory, however, until the latter part of the Triassic and the start of the Jurassic, which began about 190 million years ago. Interestingly enough, the first true mammals made their appearance at the same time. They coexisted with the dinosaurs for the rest of the Mesozoic—125 million years—but never achieved anything more than a minor role in the scheme of things. Only when the entire dinosaur population was wiped off the face of the earth did mammals get their chance.

This leaves many scientists wondering exactly what

made the dinosaurs so successful for so long. It is generally accepted that warm-blooded animals are able to sustain much higher activity levels than cold-blooded ones. It is also assumed that warm-blooded animals are more intelligent, since large, complex brains need the food, oxygen, and constant temperature an endothermic system provides. Logic therefore dictates that warm-blooded mammals should have had a tremendous evolutionary advantage and should not have had to wait for the cold-blooded dinosaurs to die out in order to come into their own. One theory, promoted by some but by no means all paleontologists, is that dinosaurs were in fact warm-blooded, that there is simply no other way the dinosaurs could have prevailed over the mammals.

If dinosaurs were not warm-blooded, the single most important factor in giving them supremacy over the other reptiles of the early Triassic may have been their gait. Once dinosaurs developed the ability to walk with their limbs straight—not sprawled out to the sides as in the crocodiles and other reptiles of the day—they had a great advantage. Their stride became much longer, and they developed a much more efficient means of walking and running than other reptiles. Also, having their legs tucked directly beneath their body provided them with a pillarlike support; this made it possible for them to get bigger and bigger. Try to imagine a creature that had a stomach the size of an Apatosaurus's along with the sprawling legs of a crocodile. The poor thing's belly would drag so far on the ground it would need a trench to walk in.

Dinosaurs may have gained supremacy over mammals and mammal-like reptiles because of a widespread climatic change in the late Triassic. Many rocks from this period are a rusty red color, like the color of those found in the southwest

The seven-year-old son of an acquaintance of mine decided he wanted to make some three-dimensional dinosaurs, so he made the fossil "bones" of all his favorite dinosaurs out of construction paper and began to assemble them in his bedroom. He had made the fossil bones large so that the dinosaurs would be about three feet high, but he soon discovered that the paper was too flimsy to stand up. Being an ingenious little dinomaniac, he began taping pieces of string to his walls and running them to the floor, creating a complex support network for his dinosaur bones.

When he finished, he had five complete dinosaurs constructed in his bedroom. He'd also turned his bedroom into something no adult could ever walk through again.

You might as well face it. If your children become heavily involved in dinosaurs, you may never enter—let alone clean— their bedrooms again.

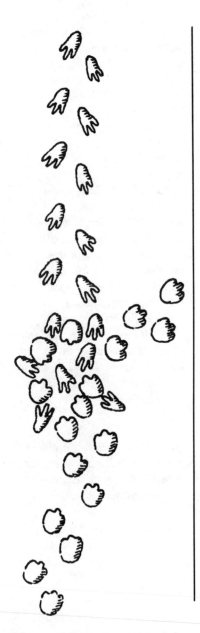

United States. Some scientists feel that this indicates widespread hot, dry weather. Reptiles have scaly skin that keeps them from dehydrating in the heat. This means they can make do with a small amount of water, and they need little food, so they are well-adapted to living in desert conditions. Mammals have a much harder time living with high temperatures, little food, and less water. This would seem to be a perfect explanation for the dinosaurs' supremacy. The only rub is that scientists who support this theory cannot yet prove that the "red rock" deposits mean that the earth was a desert in the late Triassic.

It's even possible that dinosaurs gained the throne by default. Perhaps some catastrophe caused the extinction of many of the reptiles and mammal-like reptiles but did not hurt the dinosaurs. Perhaps this hypothetical catastrophe provided the dinosaurs with an opportunity to evolve into the niches left by the animals that died out. They may have then taken over and eventually become so firmly entrenched that the mammals never had a chance to depose them.

The truth is, right now nobody knows. Still, the undeniable fact remains that dinosaurs stayed in charge for the better part of 160 million years. If you think that's not success, compare it to humans. Primates—our two-legged ancestors—have only been around for 2 or 3 million years. The first of the genus *Homo*—the humans—appeared about 2.5 million to 1 million years ago. *Homo erectus*—the first human to manage to stand on his own two feet—came on the scene somewhere between 1.5 million and 300,000 years ago. *Homo sapiens*—that's us, the "wise" humans—probably poked his head out of a cave between 300,000 and 150,000 years ago.

In just this teensy amount of time—geologically

speaking—we have come right to the brink of polluting and/
or nuking ourselves off the face of the earth. Anyone want to
bet we'll make it for another 158 million years? Las Vegas
bookies wouldn't touch it with a barge pole!

Q: If people and dinosaurs both evolved from reptiles, why don't we look like dinosaurs?

A: This is a good question. All questions about evolution
are good questions because they are very hard to answer.
And don't think that you won't be asked any. You will.
Discussions about dinosaurs are replete with references to
evolution: there is talk about how one type of dinosaur
evolved from another, like how Triceratops may have evolved
from Protoceratops; how the prosauropods seem to have been
the forerunners of the sauropods; and how birds may have
evolved from dinosaurs. It goes on and on. And at some point
your little dinomaniac is going to start wondering what he
evolved from. Even though the subject of evolution seems to
have become controversial again lately, there's no reason we
shouldn't grab the Triceratops by the horns and say—
pointedly—that dinosaurs evolved and so did we. In fact, we,
like the dinosaurs, evolved from early reptiles.

Dinosaurs, however, evolved from a different group
of early reptiles than we did. These reptiles are called
thecodonts. The thecodonts were the first archosaurs; they
were the forerunners of all the other archosaurs: the
dinosaurs, the crocodilians, and the pterosaurs. Thecodonts

The toes of the sauropods—like Apatosaurus and Diplodocus— were remarkably similar to those of certain mammals living today, like elephants.

Megalosaurus was the first dinosaur to be scientifically named and described. This was done in 1824 by an amateur paleontologist named William Buckland. In his professional life, Buckland was a famous theologian who eventually became Dean of Westminster.

were diapsids: they had two extra holes in the structure of their skulls. Mammals—and eventually humans—seem to have evolved from a group of reptiles called therapsids. Therapsids' skulls had the same number of holes as mammals' skulls do today. The therapsids are generally referred to as mammal-like reptiles.

Today, the distinctions between mammals and reptiles are very clear. In the Mesozoic, these distinctions were sometimes blurred. Although the therapsids were definitely reptiles, they had a number of mammalian characteristics. Later, another group of mammal-like reptiles called cynodonts evolved. Several members of this group had a greater number of mammalian characteristics than the therapsids did. It is difficult for paleontologists to pinpoint the exact point in evolution when certain mammal-like reptiles evolved into true mammals. Many of the characteristics that distinguish a mammal from a reptile are features like skin structure, hair, and mammary glands, which are not preserved in the fossil record. True mammals, however, had evolved by the late Triassic. One creature that was almost certainly a mammal was Megazostrodon. Scientists believe Megazostrodon was a mammal because, unlike reptiles, it had one set of baby teeth and one set of adult teeth. This indicates that it suckled its young, a true mammalian characteristic.

The majority of mammals that lived during the Mesozoic seem to have been small, nocturnal insect-eaters like Megazostrodon, which were quite similar to shrews. Only after the dinosaurs were extinct did the mammals have a chance to begin making the rapid advances—relatively speaking—that culminated in the development of the primates and, eventually, the humans.

Kinda ugly and pretty smart

The appeal of dinosaurs

After living with your little dinomaniac all these years, you undoubtedly know that dinosaurs have tremendous appeal. You just may not know why.

It's a little tough to figure out. Consider today's children, children who—thanks to our society's obsession with beauty—already think that anyone who doesn't look like Barbie or Ken is ugly, who think fat is gross, who think skin with even one pimple on it is repulsive, who wouldn't eat rare steak if it was served up at McDonald's, and who shriek in terror at the very thought of a monster with pointy teeth. Consider these children and you can't help but wonder why they have come to adore creatures who are uglier than something out of *Aliens* and fatter than a herd of hippopotami, whose skin brings new meaning to the word gross, and who went around ripping up raw red meat with long, bloody fangs and consequently must have had very bad breath.

But perhaps children don't love dinosaurs in spite of their flaws but because of them. Dinosaurs were big, they were pretty ugly, and some of them may have been kind of mean, but no parent-sized person ever picked on them! And you've got to admit, that's a characteristic with a lot of appeal.

Q: Why did dinosaurs get so big?

A: Many groups of animals throughout the history of the world have tended to evolve into larger and larger species—and that means there is an advantage to being big. This advantage is a good example of Mother Nature's logic at its best: the bigger you get, the harder it's going to be for a creature smaller than you to eat you.

This was almost certainly one of the main reasons dinosaurs evolved into such huge sizes. It protected them from a great many predators. In the wilderness today, a lone lion does not usually try to attack elephants or rhinos—they're just too big. In the same way, creatures like Allosaurus may have been discouraged from attacking the giant sauropods like Diplodocus, Apatosaurus, or Brachiosaurus unless they were still young and small or very weak.

There are a number of other speculations about the dinosaurs' size. It seems many of them may have had very big pituitary glands. Since these are the glands that regulate growth, it's possible that their size was somehow related to dinosaurs' gigantism. We know, for instance, that malfunctions of the pituitary gland can cause humans to grow beyond normal size.

It has been suggested that their large body size made it possible for dinosaurs to subsist on low-quality plant food, which may have existed in abundance in their environment. The sauropods' stomachs were so vast that they may have worked like huge fermenting tanks. When necessary, these dinosaurs may have eaten things like twigs and branches. Such high-cellulose, low-quality plant matter could have fermented in their stomach-vats for days, breaking down until

every last bit of nutrition was extracted from it.

One strange but interesting theory about why the dinosaurs got so big is that great amounts of solar radiation might have bombarded the earth during the Mesozoic and stimulated the growth of dinosaurs. This theory has an obvious hole: why didn't this alleged solar radiation cause all the dinosaurs—and all the other creatures of the day—to become giants?

It's possible that dinosaurs became huge as a means of regulating body temperature. A large mass loses heat much more slowly than a small one, so the huge dinosaurs could have soaked up the sun's heat during the day and managed to stay fairly warm throughout the night. This would be a big advantage—if these dinosaurs were cold-blooded. Most reptiles get quite cool during the night. Their muscles are stiff and sluggish in the morning until they are once again warmed by the sun. A sluggish reptile can't gather much food—and has trouble escaping if an enemy should decide to turn *him* into food.

Another reason some dinosaurs became so big may be related to the length of their lives. Many types of reptiles keep growing throughout their entire lifetime. It's possible that this continued growth may actually help them live longer. In creatures who stop growing once they reach adulthood, like humans, certain cells die out and are never replaced. But in those reptiles that never stop growing, these cells are continually replaced. This may have been true for dinosaurs, too. If so, their tendency to get bigger and bigger would have resulted in their living longer and longer—and, ultimately, in their having the opportunity to make more and more babies. And as any good scientist will tell you, animals that have an

Based on the skeletons of a herd of Maiasaura found in Alberta, paleontologists have deduced that these dinosaurs doubled their birth weight each year until adulthood and that they may have reached adult size by four years of age. This means that a fourteen-inch (36 cm) hatchling became a thirty-foot (9 m) adult in four years. If these creatures were cold-blooded, as many paleontologists still think, this growth rate would have been incredible. A cold-blooded alligator, for instance, grows at about one-tenth this speed. A warm-blooded mammal of about the same weight would grow somewhat faster than the duckbills. Some scientists think this means the hadrosaurs were warm-blooded.

opportunity to produce more offspring have a real advantage in the evolutionary scheme of things.

Q: Were dinosaurs sluggish in the morning?

A: If you haven't read much about dinosaurs since you were a kid, you probably think the answer to this question is yes. You probably think dinosaurs were sluggish all the time.

You are in trouble. The question of dinosaur sluggishness—especially morning sluggishness—has become one of the most controversial in the history of paleontology. It all relates, you see, to whether dinosaurs were warm-blooded or cold-blooded. Paleontologists everywhere are embroiled in a heated debate on the question. And kids who are really into dinosaurs are taking sides in the argument with a passion that proves that they, at least, are hot-blooded.

As of this printing, the scientific jury is still out. It seems that an increasing number of paleontologists are open to the idea that dinosaurs may have been warm-blooded, but for now, you still have to treat anyone who says that dinosaurs were undoubtedly warm-blooded with at least a little skepticism.

All reptiles living today are ectotherms—animals that get their body heat from outside sources like the sun. Endothermic animals—those who generate their own body heat—are generally mammals. Since dinosaurs are reptiles, most scientists have assumed they were also ectothermic. Recently, however, a number of paleontologists have disputed this claim. Unfortunately, it is difficult to know

Evidence of what is probably the largest amphibian that ever lived has recently been found in Germany. It existed, along with the early dinosaurs, in the middle Triassic. Although its skeleton has not yet been put together, its skull alone was four and a half feet (1.4 m) long.

which group of scientists is correct. It would help if dinosaurs' flesh and organs were preserved, but since organs and muscle tissue almost never fossilize, scientists have had to try to find something else to help them solve the problem.

In looking for clues, paleontologists have considered such things as posture, activity levels, and the ratio between predators and prey. The leading proponent of the warm-blooded theory is a renowned paleontologist named Robert Bakker. He believes that dinosaurs must have been warm-blooded because although mammals and dinosaurs evolved at about the same time, dinosaurs managed to prevail over mammals right up until their extinction. Since warm-blooded animals have so many advantages over cold-blooded ones, Bakker thinks that dinosaurs could only have gained supremacy over the mammals if they were warm-blooded too.

Bakker supports his theory, in one way, by noting that dinosaurs had an upright gait like the warm-blooded birds and mammals of today; reptiles, in contrast, still have a sprawling gait. The dinosaurs' upright gait also meant that their heads were higher than their hearts. Bakker believes that a dinosaur like Brachiosaurus would have needed a heart like endotherms have today—one with fully divided chambers—in order to pump blood up to his head; he argues that the partially divided heart typical of a reptile simply wouldn't have done the job.

Paleontologists who disagree with Bakker on these points say that a dinosaur's upright gait may have been related to size—creatures with sprawling gaits simply cannot grow to gigantic proportions—and have had nothing to do with endothermy; the chameleon, for example, is an ectotherm with an upright gait. They also suggest that

A strange and wonderful animal named Tanystropheus lived during the middle Triassic. It was not a dinosaur but a forerunner of today's lizard. Its body was less than three and a half feet (1 m) long. Its tail was quite long, but still fairly normal—about twice the length of its body. But this bizarre creature's neck was ten feet (3 m) long—as long as its tail and body put together!

Tanystropheus probably ate fish and lived close to the sea, but for some unknown reason, the young seem to have lived inland and eaten bugs and plants.

The largest crocodile ever lived during the late Cretaceous and was called Phobosuchus. Loosely translated, this means "fearsome crocodile." It lived in what is now Texas and Montana. It was fifty feet (15 m) from head to tail, and its skull alone was six feet (1.9 m) long. Imagine the teeth! It almost certainly ate dinosaurs—and anything else it could catch.

dinosaurs may have had fully divided hearts and still not have been warm-blooded.

Bakker also thinks that activity levels provide a clue to whether dinosaurs were warm- or cold-blooded. He says that any animal with a consistently high activity level must have been warm-blooded. Many paleontologists now believe that at least some dinosaurs (Deinonychus, for example) that evidently had high activity levels must have been warm-blooded. Since most ectotherms are only able to sustain short bursts of activity before their body temperature drops, this argument seems rather compelling. Bakker's opponents suggest, however, that it may have been a fully divided heart that allowed the dinosaurs to sustain high activity levels—if indeed they did.

Bakker has also considered predator-prey ratios. An endotherm needs to eat about ten times as much as an ectotherm of the same size because a great deal of an endotherm's calorie intake is used to generate body heat. Thus, a lion eats about ten times as much as a crocodile. In order to keep nature in balance, the animals that warm-blooded creatures prey on need to be ten times as numerous as the ones cold-blooded animals prey on. Bakker's estimates of predator-prey ratios in the Mesozoic seem to support his contentions. However, other highly respected paleontologists have pointed out that projecting the population of a given dinosaur simply from the number of fossils found to date involves a great deal of supposition.

Another compelling argument for endothermic dinosaurs is the similarity between the bones of dinosaurs and mammals. Cross sections of the bones of dinosaurs, mammals, and reptiles viewed under a microscope show that the first two have far more channels for carrying blood vessels than the reptile bones. It seems logical that warm-blooded animals would need to have highly vascular bone, while cold-blooded animals would not.

Bakker's suggestions along these lines stirred up so much interest in the scientific community that a number of scientists began to compare the structure of different reptile, bird, and mammal bones. Their findings have not lent support to Bakker's theories. They found that highly vascular bone was present in some reptiles as well as some—but not all—birds and mammals. They came to the conclusion that vascular bone was related more to the ability to grow rapidly and bear heavy loads—two things dinosaur bones certainly needed to do—than to endothermy.

Some paleontologists feel that the whole question of whether dinosaurs were warm- or cold-blooded is irrelevant, at least in the case of the big dinosaurs: their body size was so massive they may well have been able to retain most of the heat they absorbed from the sun for hours. That would mean that they wouldn't have been cold and sluggish in the morning at all.

And so the debate goes on. It will, no doubt, continue for quite some time. In the end, scientists may decide that some dinosaurs were warm-blooded and others were not, or they may find that dinosaurs had a system unheard of today, perhaps some combination of warm- and cold-bloodedness. It's also possible that the question will never, ever be satisfactorily answered. Regardless, scientists like Bakker have certainly stirred up an interesting controversy and done us all a favor by getting more people interested—once again—in dinosaurs.

Q: Did Tyrannosaurus eat Apatosaurus?

A: Even if you are positive you have already convinced your five year old that a dinosaur wouldn't be eating him, you have to be on your guard for any questions that have to do with what dinosaurs actually did eat. These seemingly innocent questions are, in fact, heavily loaded.

The feeling your child has for dinosaurs—as you have probably already discovered—is much more than simple fondness. It involves a kind of hero-worship. A dinosaur like Tyrannosaurus rex is a symbol of power, strength, and ferociousness. "Nobody," thinks your child, "ever spanked him!", and your child admires him for it. But if dinosaurs like Tyrannosaurus and Allosaurus are your child's heroes, then Apatosaurus, Stegosaurus, and Triceratops are his friends. And there's the rub.

Every self-respecting little dinomaniac knows that Tyrannosaurus was a meat-eater and Apatosaurus was a plant-eater. So when he comes to you holding a model of one in each hand and asks you in a quavering voice, "What did dinosaurs eat?", what he really means is "Did Tyrannosaurus eat Apatosaurus?" And to that specific question you can honestly answer "No," but only because the first Tyrannosaurus didn't come on the scene until several million years after the last Apatosaurus had gone to Apatosaurus heaven.

Your child's fears that the dinosaurs he thinks of as the "mean" meat-eaters went around eating the "peaceful" plant-eaters is, at least partially, founded. The meat-eaters were, of

Teeth were continually replaced in some—and perhaps all—dinosaurs. It seems that in the carnosaurs like Albertosaurus, the teeth were replaced alternately—in other words, two teeth in a row were never out at the same time. Thus, Albertosaurus's biting and chewing efficiency was never hampered by having too big a gap between any of his teeth. This is a system many six-year-old humans would consider a definite improvement over the way their teeth fall out.

course, not really mean—they had to eat the food that their bodies were designed to digest—but Tyrannosaurus did eat the duckbilled dinosaurs, and Allosaurus probably ate Apatosaurus and Stegosaurus, too. Indeed, paleontologists have found Apatosaurus vertebrae with Allosaurus teethmarks on them.

Still, there are several reassurances you can give your child. One is to remind him that there were things around besides other dinosaurs for the meat-eaters to eat. There were small reptiles such as lizards, reptilelike mammals, and even small mammals like Megazostrodons. Granted, it would have been awfully hard for Tyrannosaurus rex to reach down with those ridiculously short arms of his and grab a speedy little Megazostrodon, and it would have taken about a zillion of them to fill a Tyrannosaurus's tummy. Still, you can at least tell your child that there was more than Brachiosaurus burgermeat available at the local butcher shop in the days of dinosaurs.

You can also suggest that Tyrannosaurus and his friends were probably not overly greedy. After all, there were plenty of plant-eaters around at the end of the Mesozoic, so they hadn't all been eaten up. And, of course, the plant-eaters did have ways of defending themselves—but that's another question.

When your child asks you questions about what dinosaurs ate, it is possible that she isn't having horrible nightmares about the meat-eaters ripping the arms and legs off either her or her friends the peaceful plant-eaters and that all she really wants is a straightforward answer from you. If she asks, specifically, "What did the plant-eaters eat?", you can be sure you are on safe ground—nothing you say is going

It is possible that Tyrannosaurus rex may have been a scavenger because he was too massive to effectively run down his prey over long distances. If so, when the huge dinosaurs like the sauropods died naturally, the mass of decomposing flesh would have sent out an unbelievably powerful smell—so powerful, in fact, that it would have attracted tyrannosaurs from _miles_ around.

One of the biggest mysteries about sauropods is how they could consume enough food to stay alive. Some sauropods had spoon-shaped teeth, and others had peg-shaped teeth, but none of them had molars for grinding food, so they probably swallowed the pieces they bit or scraped off whole.

The largest sauropod was a good fifteen times bigger than an African elephant, an animal that needs to eat between three hundred and six hundred pounds (135–270 kg) of food a day. No one knows for sure, but even if the sauropods were cold-blooded, they may have needed to eat this much or more. If they were warm-blooded, it's possible that they would have needed to eat fifteen times as much as an elephant. Did they need to eat that much? How could they have done it? Even if they only ate a few hundred pounds of food a day, it is very difficult to imagine how they managed to do even that with such small jaws and mouths.

to terrify her. Still, you are going to have to provide her with a better answer than just "plants." She already knows that.

Depending on the time and place in which they lived, plant-eaters ate a number of different things. The teeth of big sauropods like Diplodocus indicate that they probably stripped leaves and pine needles off branches and twigs. Iguanodon's toothless, horny beak looks like it was used for cropping foliage. Stegosaurus probably browsed on ferns and cycads, the short, squat, palmlike trees that were the most common plant during the Mesozoic.

Scientists are fairly certain that the hadrosaurs—the duckbilled dinosaurs—ate leaves, twigs, pine needles, and seeds. A hadrosaur was found who had finished a tasty meal of these tidbits just before he died. This shows that hadrosaurs did not—as was once believed—live in the water and eat just the soft duckweedlike plants that they sucked and strained through their ducklike bill.

Brachiosaurus is another dinosaur once thought to have lived in the water and eaten water-plants, but paleontologists are now fairly certain that this gargantuan creature lived on land and that its long neck was adapted for nibbling leaves high in the trees.

Unfortunately, scientists will probably never know for sure which plants the herbivores ate, and they'll almost certainly never be able to tell which plants they preferred. Fossilized stomach contents are exceedingly rare, and even when they are found, there is no way for paleontologists to be certain that they are representative of the dinosaur's usual diet.

Q: How much meat could a meat-eater eat?

A: When your child asks this question, he's probably holding out some faint hope that the big carnosaurs, like Tyrannosaurus rex and Allosaurus, didn't eat *too* many of the lovable Hadrosauruses and Apatosauruses.

If the carnosaurs were cold-blooded, this may in fact be true—relatively speaking. A cold-blooded crocodile, for instance, needs to eat only one-tenth as much meat as a lion of similar size. A crocodile can wolf down a water buffalo and be content not to eat again for a number of days. The warm-blooded lion, on the other hand, might eat the same amount and be hungry again in a few hours.

Unfortunately, the debate over whether dinosaurs were warm-blooded or cold-blooded has become so hot that it's making some paleontologists' blood run cold, and we're not likely to have an answer for a long time. But there is another problem involved in trying to determine how much dinosaurs—both meat-eaters and plant-eaters—ate: how efficient they were at digesting their food.

Scientists know that dinosaurs with inefficient digestive systems would have needed to eat more than dinosaurs with efficient digestive systems; dinosaurs who ate low-quality food would have had to eat more than dinosaurs who had a source of high-quality food; and sluggish dinosaurs would have needed to eat less than speedy dinosaurs. Unfortunately, scientists can't tell us much with absolute certainty about any of these things. They don't know much about dinosaurs' digestive systems, because dinosaur stomachs—like all soft

A gastrolith is a stomach stone. It is believed that some dinosaurs—the sauropods, for instance—may have swallowed plant food whole and ground it up in a gizzard lined with gastroliths, just like some birds do today. Some smooth stones have been found lying in a position that suggests they were inside the dinosaur's stomach. Some of the stones are three inches in diameter (7 cm). A huge sauropod gizzard lined with stones of this size would surely have been heavy and may even have affected the dinosaur's posture.

tissue—almost always decayed before they could be fossilized. Even though scientists know a good deal about the plants that lived in the Mesozoic, they can't be positive which ones existed in abundance in a particular area, and they have no way of knowing which plants a particular dinosaur preferred, so they can't say much about the quality of food the dinosaurs ate. Furthermore, when it comes to the subject of dinosaurs' activity levels, many paleontologists have theories about which ones were highly active and which ones were not, but they are only theories.

Right now scientists can't be sure how much any of the dinosaurs ate, and they certainly don't know which one ate the most.

Q: Did dinosaurs like to swim?

A: The time has come to cast out your preconceived notions on the subject of dinosaurs and aquatic life. Ban forever from your mind those cherished childhood images of a beloved Brachiosaurus trotting briskly across the bottom of a fifty-foot lake. Rip every picture of every swamp-living, water-wallowing Brontosaurus out of every outdated dinosaur book you can find. The truth is now known! Scientists have taken a new look at some old information and concluded that there were no aquatic dinosaurs!

Apatosaurus may have lived near a swamp, but he didn't live in it. He may have waded in occasionally to slosh around elephant style and cool himself off, but he did not spend his life half-submerged. And Brachiosaurus's thirty-foot (9 m) neck was not the forerunner of the first man-made underwater breathing apparatus—the holes on top of his head were nostrils, not snorkels.

Now all this doesn't mean that dinosaurs couldn't swim. Some could. The duckbilled dinosaurs may well have frequently launched themselves into the water to escape from those craven carnosaurs. And scientists have found some fascinating tracks that show in detail how an Apatosaurus entered what was probably a river and floated across, lightly touching down with her front toes now and then—like a dainty little dancer—to guide herself along.

Q: Can I make my Pachycephalosaurus pink?

A: Your child can color her dinosaurs any color she wants—and nobody can prove her wrong!

Some paleontologists believe that a number of dinosaurs and other animals living in the late Mesozoic had color vision. If this is true, dinosaurs would have benefited from protective coloring that would have helped them blend in with their surroundings. Others could have used bright colors to scare off predators or attract mates, just as animals do today.

Even though the more conservative paleontologists seem to like to see dinosaurs painted in grays, greens, and browns, you needn't force your child to use these boring lizardy hues. There's no reason why dinosaurs couldn't have been as bright and boldly colored as some monitor lizards, iguanas, and Gila monsters are today. Illustrators of some of the newer dinosaur books are indulging these fancies; one has painted a hadrosaur with gold and russet mottling, colored a small,

The scientists who once believed Brachiosaurus was an aquatic animal forgot to think about water pressure. Although Brachiosaurus could have walked in water that was thirty-nine feet (12 m) deep and still have had his head out of the water so he could breathe, the water pressure on his lungs at that depth would have caused them to collapse and his blood pressure to go so high that he would have had heart failure.

An acquaintance of mine has three kids, aged nine to five, who are all dinosaur crazy. Two years ago she made them dinosaur costumes to wear for Hallowe'en, and ever since, they have insisted on wearing them for every special event that comes along.

She is mortified every time she takes her brood to an event where all the girls are wearing frilly party dresses and all the boys spiffy suits—all except her kids, who are dressed as Stegosaurus, Iguanodon, and Archaeopteryx!

swift theropod with yellow-orange, green, and shimmering violet stripes, and created a pachycephalosaur with silver skin and vibrant blue pinto designs.

The question of the color of the dinosaurs is one that cannot be answered with the information scientists have today, and it will probably never be answered—until time-travel techniques are perfected, that is.

Q: If I could touch a dinosaur, would it feel gross?

A: Well, yes, probably a little. Unless you were a dinosaur too. Then you would probably think people-skin felt gross.

Paleontologists know that at least some dinosaurs had the same kind of rough, pebbly, scaly skin many reptiles have today because they have found fossilized skin impressions. It's thought that most dinosaurs had leathery skin that was covered with scales. A mummified duckbill—an Anatosaurus—has been found that shows that this dinosaur's skin was covered with small bumps like those on a Gila monster. Bumps of varying sizes have been found on the skin of a few other duckbills.

Of course, the ankylosaurs (plated reptiles) had bony plates embedded in their skin. The ceratopsian Chasmosaurus had strange button-shaped bumps running from his neck to his tail. These buttons were two inches (5 cm) in diameter and ran in rows. No doubt these unique buttons added to Chasmosaurus's beauty. Unfortunately, those areas of his skin that were not decorated with buttons were covered with garden-variety scales.

Many of the paleontologists who think that dinosaurs were warm-blooded speculate that some species may have been covered with light fur. It's not impossible.

A few racy and radical-minded paleontologists have been spreading the rumor that dinosaurs had feathers. They have some very opinionated opinions on this subject (many of which are tied into the cold-blooded/warm-blooded debate now raging in scientific circles), and who's to say they're wrong? Scientists are only sure about the skin of those few dinosaurs who were considerate enough to lie down and die in such a way as to leave clear imprints of their skin. These dinosaurs all had lizardy skin—no feathers.

On the other hand, there are the skin—or rather feather—impressions left by Archaeopteryx. What, oh what, was Archaeopteryx, you ask? Fossil impressions of this small, feathered Jurassic creature were first found in 1861 in Germany. In 1877, an even better specimen was discovered. There could be no doubt that the creature was feathered. Subsequent studies have shown—and most paleontologists agree—that Archaeopteryx was the first bird. However, others have pointed out that Archaeopteryx has more than twenty features in common with the small theropod dinosaurs, the coelurosaurs. In fact, some paleontologists claim that if Archaeopteryx's feathers had not been visible in the fossil impressions, it almost certainly would have been classified as a theropod dinosaur. Other paleontologists are absolutely *convinced* it was a feathered dinosaur and not a bird at all. Some scientists feel Archaeopteryx helps prove that birds evolved directly from the dinosaurs—and so dinosaurs are not extinct at all!

So, did dinosaurs have feathers? Until some dedicated

Instead of having a beak like a modern bird, Archaeopteryx, which means "ancient wing," had a long, narrow snout. She was about the size of a large crow, but her jaw was lined with sharp teeth, and there were three claws on the front of her wings.

paleontologist digs up a feathered skin impression from a creature that was without any doubt a dinosaur, I'm afraid the debate is going to rage on. In the meantime, if your child insists on putting feathers on the dinosaurs in his coloring books, why insist otherwise?

Q: Did dinosaurs wag their tails?

A: According to teachers I know, children have suddenly become fascinated with dinosaur tails and the question of how said tails were held. They want to know if—as pictures in the more enlightened dinosaur books are now indicating—dinosaurs could really hold their tails straight out behind them when they ran or if in fact they dragged their tails on the ground, as the majority of picture books still indicate.

When your child first comes to you with a question about dinosaur tails, don't laugh. Don't say, "Who cares?" Dinosaurs could do some amazing things with their tails.

It is now known that most bipedal dinosaurs did indeed hold their tails up and straight out behind them for balance when they were walking or running. Although some may have put their tails on the ground and used them as a kind of brace when they were standing still, others, like Tenontosaurus, could not have done this because their tails were too stiff.

It is thought that many of the fleet-footed bipedal dinosaurs like Struthiomimus and Deinonychus actually used their tails as a dynamic stabilizer when they were running. The front of the body was stretched forward and was counterbalanced by the weight of the tail. The tail helped keep

Cheeks were an extremely important development in dinosaur evolution. The primitive Triassic plant-eating ornithopods like Fabrosaurus had no cheeks, so they could not really chew their food—it would simply fall out of their mouths if they tried. They must have had to swallow twigs and leaves in big chunks that were very hard to digest. Later, similar dinosaurs, like Hypsilophodon, had cheek pouches and better teeth. These seemingly small advances made them far more efficient and successful animals.

them steady at top speeds. Also, the shape of the body when it was stretched out in this way was very aerodynamically efficient.

Specialized bony structures in the tails and hips of Deinonychus and Struthiomimus made it possible for their tails to be both stiff and flexible. This adaptation probably allowed them to use their tails to stabilize their bodies even when they were turning at top speeds. It is thought that Deinonychus, for instance, could rotate the front end of his body, thereby allowing him to change directions extremely rapidly just by swinging his tail from side to side. No matter how desperately Deinonychus's prey dodged and feinted, it almost never escaped. Deinonychus could, as they say, turn on a dime.

The question of what the quadrupedal dinosaurs did with their tails when running is another matter. Some paleontologists think that the quadrupeds ran with their tails extended just like the bipeds. Others disagree. They think that most quadrupeds—and certainly the huge sauropods like Apatosaurus—dragged their tails behind them just like they do in the old picture books.

This is yet another dinosaur-sized controversy that may never be solved.

Q: What sound did a dinosaur make?

A: This is another one of those hard-to-know-the-answer-for-sure questions. It's hard to answer at all. But some paleontologists have made a few guesses. One paleontologist recently made an exact replica of the three-foot-long (1 m)

Joseph Leidy, an American, described the Hadrosaurus in 1858. He realized that this creature must have stood more like a kangaroo than an elephant and created the first really accurate picture of dinosaurs' posture.

A friend of mine has a two and a half year old who has been seriously "into" dinosaurs for several months. He likes his mom to play with his plastic dinosaurs with him. She gets right into the act, scooting the little models around the floor and making great growling noises.

As often as not, however, the sounds she makes upset the boy. Oh, it's not that he's scared. He is convinced that he knows whether the sounds she is making are the ones the dinosaurs actually made or not. It seems that she is forever getting them wrong, and he is constantly having to correct her. "No, Mommy, no!" he yells. "Stegosaurus sounded this." He then patiently makes the correct dinosaur sound and gets her to practise it until he thinks she has it right.

The boy is so adamant about these sounds that she is beginning to get the feeling that the kid is tuning in on some bizarre wavelength to the music of the Mesozoic.

tube that juts out of the duckbill Parasaurolophus's head. He found that blowing into the tube produced a strange, resonating sound, not unlike the haunting sound of the long horn used by the mountain people in the Alps. There is also a theory that other duckbills had inflatable—and perhaps brightly colored—flaps of skin covering their nostrils. These flaps may have worked like resonators to make loud reverberating snorts, perhaps something like the roar of an elephant seal.

Just what sounds other dinosaurs made is anybody's guess. I can't imagine a huge carnosaur that didn't rant, roar, and snarl. Perhaps the parrot-faced dinosaurs like Protoceratops and Psittacosaurus squawked. Iguanodon, with that horselike snout of his, looks like he might have been a squealer. In between raucous burps, Apatosaurus and Diplodocus look like they might have made dainty mooing sounds like a newborn calf. Triceratops was probably pretty quiet unless provoked, but then he could probably snort and bellow with the best of them.

Even if nobody is sure exactly what kinds of sounds the dinosaurs made, I'll bet they made noise, and plenty of it. I just don't believe that the world of the Mesozoic could have been a very quiet place.

Q: Did dinosaurs get to be as old as you, Dad?

A: The answer to this question illustrates an all-too-frequent state of affairs in familial circles: kids don't understand that terms like "old" are relative. The question also represents an all-too-frequent state of affairs in paleontological circles: paleontologists don't know the answer.

There is, of course, no shortage of intrepid paleontologists who are willing to make a guess. Some paleontologists believe that dinosaurs, like turtles, lived to be very old indeed. Some say those dinosaurs who had a relatively slow-paced lifestyle could have lived for centuries. Indeed, growth rings found on some dinosaur bones seem to indicate that certain species could have lived for at least 120 years.

Other paleontologists don't think that any dinosaurs had a slow-paced lifestyle. Some of them think that dinosaurs were hot-blooded beasts that raced around at great speeds ripping limbs off every tree—and animal—that happened to get in their way. It's hard to imagine them living—or wanting to live—at this pace for centuries.

The safest answer is probably that some kinds of dinosaurs may have lived to a great old age, while others did not. Some species may have been capable of living a long time but didn't because they got eaten up first. Others may have survived for a century or more. Other species may have had naturally short life spans. A well-known paleontologist speculates that Maiasaura, a hadrosaur that was preyed upon by the great carnosaurs, may have had to age rapidly in order to reach sexual maturity, breed, and replenish its numbers with new babies. If this was the case, a ten-year-old Maiasaura would have been thought, by the youngsters, to be a veritable Methuselah.

Q: Were dinosaurs dumb?

A: When your child first hears that his two-ton friend Stegosaurus had a brain about the size of a golf ball (kindly estimates) or perhaps the size of a walnut (unkindly estimates), it may hit him hard. It may, in fact, hit him harder than the news about Santa. You'll need to handle the situation with care, especially if your child clings, with desperate hope, to the notion that Stegosaurus had a second—big—brain in his hindquarters.

The truth of the matter is that this second so-called brain was not a brain at all. It was simply an enlargement of the spinal cord that acted as a relay station for messages sent from Stegosaurus's pea-sized—excuse me, walnut-sized—brain to its nether regions. But even though it wasn't a brain, this enlarged spinal area *was* helpful: Stegie was very adept at whipping that spiked tail of his around.

You can also comfort your child with the idea that, whatever the size of Stegosaurus's brain, it was every bit as big as he needed. After all, his species endured for a good 11 million years. That's far better than *Homo sapiens,* who has probably only been around 150,000 years.

Your preschool paleontologist will probably want to know about the brain sizes of more dinosaurs than Stegosaurus. If this is the case, you may—depending on the size of your child's brain—want to discuss a little something called encephalization quotients. This is a rating system that relates the estimated size of a dinosaur's brain to his body weight and comes up with a rough indication of intelligence. Using the EQ, scientists can compare dinosaurs with reptiles and other animals living today.

While it is true that dinosaurs like Stegosaurus and Triceratops don't come out too well on the EQ scale—they get a 0.2—they do rate a bit higher than Diplodocus and Brachiosaurus, who only rate a 0.1. Tyrannosaurus and Allosaurus do quite a bit better with a rating of 0.9. That's just a little less than the EQ of a lion. Several dinosaurs fall in the 0.6 range; many mammals living today aren't much higher than that. A kangaroo's EQ, for instance, falls somewhere around 0.7. And Troödon's EQ is a whopping 5.3! Good for you Troödon! Way to think!

We can't infer from this that dinosaurs were actually as intelligent as mammals with similar EQs—there are simply too many other factors and "unknowns" involved—but the comparison certainly provides food for thought, so to speak.

There was clearly a wide range of intelligence among the different types of dinosaurs, and many had respectably sized brains. Iguanodon, for instance, was in the 0.6 range; this means that his brain size compares favorably with the EQ of reptiles living today. Now the intelligence of the average reptile may not be something that generally puts you in a state of awe, but scientists have recently discovered that some reptiles are capable of far more complex social behavior than ever before believed, and this is proof positive that we do not have the right to dismiss dinosaurs as being dumb.

The Nile crocodile, for instance, has an EQ of approximately 0.9—about the same as Tyrannosaurus's. They were once thought to be capable of nothing more than basking in the sun and biting off a swimmer's leg every now and then. But no. Nile crocs are downright bright. Well, if not actually bright, they are at least capable of amazingly complex social behavior. The males, for instance, don't become

The dumb dinosaur rumor has been around since the 1880s. The legendary paleontologist O. C. Marsh may have been instrumental in starting it. In 1879, he discovered a large number of Stegosaurus bones. Later he made a cast of a brain from one of the skulls. To his amazement, he realized the brain could have weighed no more than a few ounces, and yet the dinosaur probably weighed a good 1.6 tons (1.5 t)—perhaps even more.

The sediments surrounding the Maiasaura nests in Montana were a reddish color, but the nests, which were constructed from these same sediments, are green. It's possible that the color change was caused by a reaction between the iron minerals and the plant matter brought to the nests to feed the babies.

interested in females until the males are twelve to fifteen years of age. They then compete for the most desirable females with ritualized displays of aggression, much like many birds and advanced mammals (including a lot of humans), in order to determine who gets first choice, second choice, and so on. The crocodiles then choose their partners. But the females are very selective and will only mate after an elaborate courtship ritual (much more elaborate, for instance, than anything you'll see in a singles bar). The females mate with one—and only one—male. The male is faithful, too, and hangs around his female and visits her after she builds her nest. He doesn't get too close to the nest—after all, he doesn't want to intrude—but he does stay in the neighborhood for the entire three-month nesting period.

The female lays her eggs—as many as eighty—in the mud about twenty inches (50 cm) deep. She then tends the nest tirelessly for the entire three months, probably not even leaving to find food. When the babies finally begin hatching they call to Mama from deep down in the mud, and she quickly—but oh so carefully—digs them up. She then gently carries each one to the water, washes it off, and lets it swim back to shore. Papa realizes the time has come for him to approach the nest, and he actually helps Mama with the fetching, carrying, and washing of babies. If some of the youngsters are having a tough time cracking their eggs, Mama or Papa pick up the eggs one by one and gently roll them around in their mouths until the shell begins to crack.

The proud parents care for their hatchlings for about two months. The babies then leave the nest to join the other youngsters from the area, forming a communal group that works co-operatively to build burrows in the sand banks where they can retreat from danger.

If the reptiles of today are capable of this kind of complex behavior, there is no reason why those dinosaurs with brains of relatively the same proportions could not have done just as much. Troödon was probably as intelligent as many birds are today, and birds are quite smart: the smartest birds can be trained to do tricks and mimic human speech.

So it seems we must banish, once and for all, two myths: first, that dinosaurs were dumb, and second, that they had two brains. Still, we can be forgiven if we occasionally chuckle over some of the colorful images these mistaken ideas have conjured up:

> Behold the mighty dinosaur,
> Famous in prehistoric lore,
> Not only for his power and strength
> But for his intellectual length.
> You will observe by these remains
> The creature had two sets of brains—
> One in his head (the usual place),
> The other at his spinal base.
> No problem bothered him a bit
> He made both head and tail of it.
> If something slipped his forward mind
> 'Twas rescued by the one behind.
> And if in error he was caught
> He had a saving afterthought.
> Thus he could think without congestion
> Upon both sides of every question.*

*Excerpt from a poem by B. L. Taylor, quoted in McGowan, *The Successful Dragons*, 131.

The appeal of dinosaurs 49

"Do dinosaurs eat kids?"

And other dinosaur questions to avoid at bedtime

Questions to avoid at bedtime include any that contain key words such as "teeth," "claws," and "eat me." Anytime your child asks you a question containing one of these words, be aware that you are about to enter a classic no-win situation. If you don't find some way to soothe your child's fears—and nip the conversation in the bud—you're going to find yourself with an extra person in your bed all night.

The worst possible thing you can do is to get so caught up in answering your child's questions that you forget you are going to be turning out the lights in a few minutes. Here's how conversations like this invariably evolve:

Daddy: Good night. Sweet dreams.

Son: I just want to ask you one thing about dinosaurs.

Daddy: Yes, son?

Son: Did dinosaurs have fangs?

Daddy: Well, I guess you could call them fangs. Fangs are just big, sharp teeth, and some of the meat-eaters did have pretty big, sharp teeth. So, yes, you could call them fangs—but I think we should just call them teeth, don't you?

Son: How long were the meat-eaters' fangs?

Daddy: They varied. Little meat-eaters had little teeth and big meat-eaters had big teeth. Some of Tyrannosaurus's teeth were about six inches long.

Son: Is six inches about as long as my face?

Daddy: Well, uh, yes.

Son: Daddy, what did these teeth look like exactly?

Daddy: The teeth of the meat-eating dinosaurs were pointed and sharp. Some were almost like the blade of a knife. Others were like daggers and had serrated edges.

Son: What are serrated edges?
Daddy: They're like the edges on a steak knife.
Son: Does that mean a meat-eater could slice me up as fast as you slice up my steak?
Daddy: No more questions about teeth.

Clearly daddy's no-more-questions-about-teeth retort has come too late. Teeth questions have to be stopped long before you get to the subject of serrated edges. Besides, teeth questions invariably lead to the question of whether any dinosaurs are alive today. And it doesn't matter how many times you tell a child who is about to go to sleep that there are no dinosaurs alive today, he won't believe you. His eyes open wide and his voice speeds up until he sounds like Alvin the Chipmunk and the questions start rolling like this: "But how can you be sure? Have you been everywhere in the whole wide world? Well then, how do you know there isn't a dinosaur somewhere where you haven't been? What if the Loch Ness monster is a dinosaur? How do you know there's no such thing as the Loch Ness monster? If there was such a thing as the Loch Ness monster, could it get out of Loch Ness? How long does it take to get from Loch Ness to here? What if it took an airplane? How do you know they wouldn't let it on the plane? What if it hijacked the plane? How long does it take to get from the airport to our street? How do you know the army wouldn't let it get out of the airport? What if the Loch Ness monster-dinosaur could breathe fire? What if it breathed fire on the army and melted all their guns and all their tanks and all their bombers? Then what?"

Yeah, Dad, then what? Nighty-night? Sweet dreams? No way. Take my advice: avoid bedtime questions about teeth, fangs, claws, and meat-eaters' eating habits at all costs!

Q: Did dinosaurs eat kids?

A: Some of them would have if they could have. But—thank goodness—they couldn't have. Dinosaurs did not live at the same time as people. In fact, the last dinosaur had disappeared off the face of the earth a good 62 million years before the first caveman poked his head out of a cave.

Still the vicious rumor persists that Tyrannosaurus rex and his buddies munched cavemen, cavewomen, and—heaven forbid—tasty little cavechildren for breakfast, lunch, and dinner. According to the guides at places like Alberta's Dinosaur Provincial Park, this silly bit of slander is the bane of their existence. They say it has caused countless kiddies to fall asleep in the park campground with visions of something much nastier than sugarplums dancing in their heads. And the guides know exactly who to blame for spreading this malicious misinformation: not a faulty education system, not inadequately trained teachers, not disinterested parents. No, they lay the blame right where it belongs: squarely on the square shoulders of Fred Flintstone. Yes, Fred and his fellow citizens of Bedrock—Barney, Wilma, Betty, Pebbles, and BamBam—are to blame. They instigated the rumor that man, woman, and dinosaur lived at the same time, that you could have a Stegosaurus for a pet, and that you could work in a gravel pit where you drove a Brachiosaurus and operated him like a crane.

A friend took his four-year-old niece to see the dinosaur exhibit at a museum one day. As she looked up at the huge creatures, she clutched his hand so tightly that she cut off the circulation to his fingers. He knew she was scared, but he didn't quite know what to say, so he just put a comforting arm around her shoulders. Finally, she tugged on his hand and said, "Well, now I know why there were no people around when there were dinosaurs."

"Why's that?" he asked.

She looked up, her brown eyes huge, and said, "The people were _way_ too scared."

Q: Could I run faster than a dinosaur?

A: This question is sometimes disguised as "How fast could a dinosaur run?", "Which dinosaur could run the fastest?", or, more to the point, "Which meat-eater could run the fastest?" Regardless, what your child really wants to know is whether he could get away if a dinosaur were chasing him. Of course, he knows a dinosaur wouldn't ever really be chasing him, but he still wants to know the answer to this question—just in case.

Unfortunately for you—if you are determined to answer your child's questions honestly—several of the great carnosaurs could probably run as fast, or much faster, than a human. There's a good chance Allosaurus would have been able to catch a man for dinner—if there had been any men around. Albertosaurus would almost certainly have been able to overtake a hypothetical human, even one running as fast as his about-to-be-eaten legs could carry him.

Our hypothetical human wouldn't have had a snowball's chance in Texas against Acrocanthosaurus, a carnosaur whose trackways were found in that very state. Estimates from these tracks suggest that Acrocanthosaurus was probably capable of running up to twenty-five miles (40 km) per hour. Acrocanthosaurus may have been the speediest carnosaur.

There's not much good news in all this for the parent who has to answer this question at bedtime, but it is possible that a fit, muscular, well-toned human might have been able to outrun a Tyrannosaurus—a useful bit of information to have on hand when your child refuses to go to gym class.

Dinosaur tracks have been found in Morocco of a dinosaur that has been given the name Breviparopus. One paleontologist speculates—from the length of the creature's stride—that Breviparopus could have been 157 feet (48 m) long. That would make him even longer than the famed dinosaur nicknamed Ultrasaurus. Other paleontologists say such a claim is ridiculous since no bones of the dinosaur have been found: the long stride may well have been made by a running Breviparopus. The stride of a running creature is much longer than that of one walking.

Some paleontologists think that the swiftest dinosaur of all may have been Gallimimus, a beaked dinosaur who may have eaten insects and eggs. His tremendous speed allowed him to escape from his predators. Gallimimus was about thirteen feet (4 m) long. He was the largest ornithomimosaur—those dinosaurs whose bodies were shaped strangely like those of ostriches. Of course, they had arms instead of wings and long, thick tails, but their legs were long like an ostrich's, and they had very similar large, powerfully built thighs. It has been calculated that Gallimimus would have been able to run up to 35 miles (56 km) per hour.

Other paleontologists think that the theropod Troödon, formerly known as Stenonychosaurus, may have been the fastest runner. This meat-eater was only about six feet (1.8 m) long and probably only a little over three feet (1 m) high at the hips, but he may well have been one of the most fearsome of dinosaurs. He had a very large brain, excellent eyesight, and good-sized sicklelike claws. He probably hunted in packs and attacked dinosaurs much bigger than himself with what can only be considered admirable confidence. He too had legs that remind you of an ostrich's. Some scientists think he could have outrun one of these present-day birds—and their speed has been estimated at as high as fifty miles (80 km) per hour.

Even though scientists can only estimate the speed at which dinosaurs could travel, they can make rather good guesses when they have the fossilized tracks of a particular dinosaur and know exactly how long its legs were. They measure the length between two of the prints of the same foot. This gives them the stride length. The longer the stride length, the faster the animal was moving. Some estimates of speed are based on a comparison between the length and

Kids are often torn between love and fear of dinosaurs. When Dinamation, an exhibit of automated, roaring dinosaurs, was held at the Royal Ontario Museum, the display was roped off and set in a simulated Mesozoic woodland environment. One of the guides from the museum's visitor services department saw a little girl, who appeared to be about five years old, pull her little brother toward the dinosaurs. He stared at the display in fascination, but he was also crying and yelling, "Are they alive? Are they alive?"

As she pulled him closer, she scolded, "Of course they're alive, you ninny! But don't be scared. They've got those ropes to keep them in."

shape of the dinosaur's legs and those of animals with similar legs today. To a certain degree, an animal can run faster the longer and more slender his legs are.

It's highly unlikely that the huge sauropods could have run anywhere near as fast as a long- and slender-legged creature like Gallimimus. The weight of their bodies would have put a tremendous strain on their legs when they ran. One estimate is that an Apatosaurus may have been able to walk about seven and a half miles (12 km) per hour. A human can walk, for a short distance, at speeds of up to fifteen miles (24 km) per hour.

It's clear that dinosaurs weren't the slow, plodding, lethargic creatures it was once believed. If they were warm-blooded, they may even have zipped hither and yon all day long.

Q: Who was the toughest dinosaur of all?

A: I don't want to burst any bubbles here, but it's quite possible that Tyrannosaurus rex was not the toughest dinosaur. Oh, he was tough, all right, but there is some evidence that he only ripped the arms and legs and heads off dinosaurs that were already dead. If this is true, it means he was—I hate to say it—nothing more than a scavenger.

An alternative choice for the fiercest, meanest dinosaur is Deinonychus. This early Cretaceous theropod was only about five feet (1.5 m) tall and nine feet (2.7 m) long and weighed only about as much as the average man of the house does today. But in spite of her relatively small size, Deinonychus

Tyrannosaurus rex was fifty feet (15 m) long, but his arms were only thirty inches (76 cm) long. They were so short that T. rex could not even scratch his chin.

was one of the most extraordinary predators of all time. This swift, keen-eyed creature had big jaws and large, serrated teeth. She was capable of a terrible, snapping bite. Her teeth were curved backwards, expressly for ripping off large chunks of flesh. She had strong, grasping hands, with long claws on each of her three fingers, and her arms were so strong that it is almost certain that she used them to embrace victims that were struggling most desperately to escape.

But her most amazing feature was a five-inch-long (13 cm), sickle-shaped claw on her hind legs. This claw worked a bit like a switchblade and could be held in an upright position when Deinonychus was running. Paleontologists can tell from the way certain of her leg muscles attached that her hind legs could kick, powerfully, downward and backward—just the motion for stabbing into and then ripping open her victim's soft, unprotected underbelly.

She was also an extremely agile dinosaur. Her tail, which she held straight out behind her when she ran, worked as a kind of dynamic stabilizer. By swinging it from side to side, she was able to rotate the front of her body and rapidly change direction, even when she was running at full speed.

There is also evidence that Deinonychuses travelled in packs so that they could attack a large plant-eater by swarming all over him. Some would grab the victim's tail in order to slow him down, others would jump on his back or nip at his hindquarters, while the most ferocious leapt at his stomach and eviscerated the hapless creature while he was still alive.

I trust you'll tone down this information before sharing it with your children.

The most dangerous creature of the late Triassic may have been, not a meat-eating dinosaur, but a reptile named Rutiodon. This creature was only about twelve feet (3.5 m) long, but he had crocodile-like jaws and sharp teeth. His body was protected by bony plates, and he was probably very aggressive.

Q: Did all dinosaurs have big claws?

A: There is simply no reassuring way to answer this question. The thought of dinosaur claws seems to scare kids even more—if possible—than the thought of dinosaur teeth. Kids who chuckled all the way through *Aliens* cringe at the mention of dinosaur claws.

And all dinosaurs—even the plant-eaters—had claws. Some dinosaur claws were very big indeed. Others were just deadly. If you read the answer to the preceding question, you already know about Deinonychus and her horrible sickle-shaped switchblade/claw. But there is worse news in the claw department.

In 1965, another dinosaur with a terrible claw was discovered in the Gobi Desert. Only the arms and hands of this dinosaur have been found—but they stretch out to a length of nine feet (3 m). Each finger was armed with sharp, hooked claws that were eight to twelve inches (20–30 cm) long. One paleontologist wrote that he shuddered to think what the whole beast must have looked like. It may have been one of the most dangerous dinosaurs that ever lived. Since the word for terrible claw had already been used for Deinonychus, paleontologists have named this creature Deinocheirus, which means terrible hand.

An even scarier claw was found in Surrey, England, in 1983. This sickle-shaped, dagger-pointed claw was uncovered by an amateur collector, who must have had a bit of a shock when he saw the size of the thing—it's over twelve inches (30 cm) long! Paleontologists have recently given this dinosaur the name *Baryonyx walkeri*. "Baryonyx" means heavy claw, and "walkeri" refers to Bill Walker, the man who

The Gorgo of horror-movie fame seems to have gotten his name from the dinosaur Gorgosaurus, whose name means "terrible lizard." Unfortunately, it turns out that Gorgosaurus was really an Albertosaurus.

There's no doubt that Albertosaurus was a fearsome carnosaur—but Albert would never have made it in the movies.

found it. Baryonyx's claws are huge in proportion to his body. He is estimated to have been about twenty-seven to thirty feet (9–10 m) long and about nine to twelve feet (3–4 m) tall. One of the interesting things about Baryonyx is that he seems to have been a fish-eater; the remains of a fish over three feet (1 m) long were found in his stomach. No other dinosaurs are known fish-eaters—but then again, we know little about dinosaurs' diets. Baryonyx's teeth and jaws had a great deal in common with a crocodile's. It's possible that he crouched at the edge of the water or waded in the shallows and snatched at fish with his fearsome claws, just like a giant grizzly bear.

The big sauropods like Apatosaurus all had one or more claws on their front feet and three or more on their back feet, but they probably used them for peaceful purposes like nest-building.

As a group, the lizard-hipped dinosaurs tended to have blunt claws that protected their toes, just like animals' hoofs do today. But Iguanodon had a large and unusual spiked claw on each thumb. Iguanodon, who was generally a gentle kind of guy, may have used his thumb-spikes to poke his enemies in the neck or eyes when they provoked him.

A gigantic fossilized arm and several claws were found recently in Mongolia. The dinosaur they belonged to has been given the name Therizinosaurus, which means "scythe lizard." The arm was about eight feet (2.5 m) long, and some of the claws were thirty inches (75 cm) long—as long as a scythe used for cutting grass!

Q: How did the peaceful plant-eaters keep from getting shredded to bits by the mean meat-eaters?

A: As we have already unfortunately established, many of them didn't. Still there's some good news: some of them did. And here's how.

The big sauropods like Apatosaurus and Diplodocus had their size going for them. An average Allosaurus was about sixteen and a half feet (5 m) tall. This means that he would have just reached the top of an Apatosaurus's hips. But if the Apatosaurus reared up on his hind legs, he would literally have towered above the Allosaurus and could have crashed down on the carnosaur's head with his front feet. What's more, "Pat" outweighed "Al" by about seven to one. There is also evidence from fossil tracks that tells us that Apatosaurus and some other plant-eaters had the good sense to travel in herds. A lone meat-eater—no matter how big or how fierce—would have had to have been foolish indeed to mess with a whole herd of Apatosauruses.

Most of the large sauropods probably also had tough, leathery—not to mention thoroughly unappetizing—skin. This gave them added protection. Some sauropods were able to use their long tails as formidable whips. Diplodocus's tail, for instance, was forty-five feet (13.5 m) long and had unusual, chevron-shaped vertebrae that made it extremely flexible.

Other plant-eaters had more obvious forms of protection. Stegosaurus's strong, thick tail was definitely designed for thrashing about—and it was tipped with four sharply pointed spikes that were each over three feet (1 m) long. In addition, Stegosaurus had those huge triangular plates running up and down his back. While these plates probably didn't offer much protection, they surely made Stegosaurus look like a very scary guy. There's no doubt about it, an Allosaurus would have had to be awfully hungry before he tried to make ground steak out of a Stegosaurus.

The plated dinosaurs like Stegosaurus died out at the end of the Jurassic, and the next generation of plant-eaters evolved some exceptional protective devices. The Ankylosaurs—also known as the armored dinosaurs—compare favorably to Sherman tanks. Two of the most famous herbivores, Ankylosaurus and Nodosaurus, had bony plates and/or spiky studs all over their bodies. One of their cousins, Euoplocephalus, even had bone-plated eyelids.

These dinosaurs also had powerful, flexible tails. Ankylosaurus's was equipped with a massive club on the end, and some of his relatives' tails had both clubs and spikes. Those medieval knights who thought they were so clever to have invented the mace would have been chagrined if they'd known that a relatively small-brained dinosaur had beat them to the—a-hem!—punch by about 64 million years.

Triceratops was another well-protected Cretaceous plant-eater. Hardly anyone wanted to eat him. He is believed to have been a quiet, unaggressive creature—unless and until he was provoked. Then he may well have charged a full-grown Tyrannosaurus with nary a hint of nervous perspiration. Triceratops was considerably smaller than Tyrannosaurus— about half the size and two-thirds the weight—but his massive head must have been horrifying. It made up a full third of his twenty-five foot (7.5 m) length. The huge frill around his neck made his head look even more formidable, and two of his horns were forty inches (102 cm) long.

You can safely tell your child that his friend Triceratops, at least, had no real enemies.

Some of the hadrosaurs, or duckbill dinosaurs, may have had as many as two thousand teeth in their mouths!

Prehistoric love

The most often asked dinosaur questions

Children seem to want to know the strangest things about dinosaurs, like whether they went out on dates. Now, questions about a dinosaur's personal life seem funny to us, but that's only because we've forgotten that dinosaurs are just like people—at least to our children.

And that means we darned well better not laugh when our children ask questions about prehistoric love. No matter that these questions conjure up wonderfully ludicrous images in our brains: two Brachiosauruses with their forty-foot necks entwined; an Allosaurus sheepishly shuffling his feet as he hands his beloved a bouquet made of cycad fronds, or maybe ripping a drumstick off a Stegosaurus for her to show his goodwill and the honorableness of his intentions; a Triceratops beauty queen presiding over the spring courtship ritual and taking her pick of the bevy of beautiful boys that parade, flip their frills, and strut their stuff before her admiring eyes.

No, we had better not laugh at this stuff. At least not in front of our kids. To them, prehistoric intimacy is a very serious subject. And when they ask about it, they want answers—real answers. So here's the lowdown on some highly emotional stuff: dinosaur love and marriage.

Q: Did dinosaurs go on dates?

A: They did go on dates. Sort of. At least they may have had fairly elaborate courtship rituals. While many of these rituals may not have been on a par with the bouquets and boxes of candy of yesteryear, they were certainly as advanced as those exhibited by the average motorcycle punk of today, since this creature's courtship rituals usually involve nothing more complex than screeching to a halt in front of his potential mate's suburban lair and cranking up his ghettoblaster a few hundred decibels.

Although there's no proof that all dinosaurs engaged in courtship rituals, it is almost certain that some did. Some of the clues to the existence of this behavior lie in the strange horns, frills, and headdresses found on dinosaurs like the hadrosaurs, the ceratopsians, and the pachycephalosaurs. The hadrosaurs had head-crests that looked like everything from the meat platter on Corythosaurus to the flattened-out teakettle on Lambeosaurus. Parasaurolophus had a long tube that extended over three feet (1 m) back from his head.

While these crests may have had a variety of purposes, one function was almost certainly to provide visual—and possibly auditory—signals during mating seasons. Many different kinds of duckbills lived together in the same area, and the distinctive crests would have prevented confusion when the dinosaurs were trying to meet and mate with members of their own species.

A few of the more flat-headed duckbills may have actually butted heads while competing for position in the social order and for particular females, but most of the hadrosaurs probably relied on "ritualized" combat. Instead of actually fighting, the species with magnificent-looking headdresses may have paraded proudly, and those who could make sounds through their crests trumpeted out their longing in strange, prehistoric love songs.

The pachycephalosaurs were, perhaps, a bit more crude. They almost certainly used those thick, bone-plated heads of theirs to compete for territory and females. The males probably butted heads and rammed each other just as mountain goats do during mating season today. Still, their courtship battles were ritualized—in other words, they didn't really hurt each other with all that butting about and banging of heads.

The ceratopsians, like Triceratops, Pentaceratops, and Chasmosaurus, may well have used their horns to fend off predators. The magnificent frills that jutted out over their necks may have also given them some protection. The frills also provided a place for the ceratopsians' huge neck muscles to attach—and without them they couldn't have carried around their huge heads and heavy horns—but their horns and frills were probably equally important in establishing social hierarchy and in attracting females. Triceratops, for instance, probably locked horns in ritualized combat much as male antelopes do today, and the ceratopsians like Chasmosaurus, with those strange and wonderful long frills, may have simply wagged their heads and strutted their stuff like peacocks—or certain colorful, spiky-haired creatures we know and love today.

Paleontologists have a tough time telling male dinosaurs from female dinosaurs. But in the case of Protoceratops, an early relative of Triceratops, they can tell the difference. They have discovered that the males had bumps on their noses and the females did not.

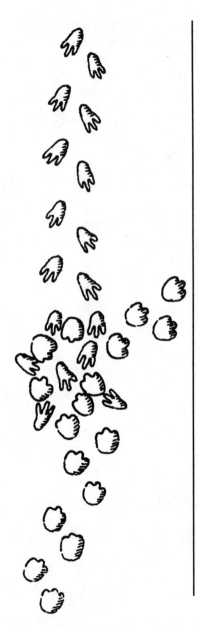

Q: How did dinosaurs make babies?

A: For some reason, people who get a little tongue-tied when asked questions about reproduction seem to lose the power of speech completely the instant the image of two thirty-ton, copulating Apatosauruses flashes across their mind.

But you might as well be prepared. Museum guards from around the country say they get asked about dinosaur reproduction more frequently than about any other subject, and your child is going to ask about it sooner or later, too. If you are one of the many people who find it hard to talk about the birds and the bees, you might as well hope for "sooner"— if it's "later," you'll have to go into more detail.

When your child asks you this question, you can answer briefly—and honestly—by saying "Nobody knows." But that's a cop-out, and your prepubescent paleontologist is going to know it.

Museum guards often answer questions about dinosaur reproduction by saying, "Dinosaurs probably made babies much like reptiles do today." This is a good answer as far as it goes. But how do reptiles reproduce?

In reptilian reproduction, the male reptile's sperm fertilizes the female's eggs in the oviduct, which is inside the female's body; reptiles' eggs are not fertilized outside the body as some fish eggs are. Reptiles have a variety of methods for getting the sperm into the oviduct. When tuataras—creatures from New Zealand that look a lot like a lizard—mate, they press their cloacae together and the sperm flows from the male into the female. The cloaca, by the way, is a simple kind of vent.

All other male reptiles have a special structure that helps

facilitate the passage of the sperm into the female's oviduct. Some, like turtles and crocodiles, have a primitive type of penis that consists of spongelike material. It is located just inside the male's cloaca. When it fills with blood it expands and can be inserted into the female's cloaca to guide the sperm into place.

Male lizards and snakes have a structure called a hemipenis. Each male has two of them at the base of his tail. They are hollow tubes located beneath the skin. During mating, one hemipenis expands and turns outward, much like a finger on a glove that is turned inside out but that can be pushed out to its regular position. The hemipenis is then inserted into the female's cloaca.

One of the most interesting things about reptile reproduction is that a number of female reptiles have small glands or tubes in the oviduct where they can store sperm. Female turtles and snakes in captivity have been known to lay fertile eggs after being separated from males for as long as six years!

A few species of female lizards even seem to be able to reproduce without males. As far as scientists know, there are no males in these species. All the eggs scientists have observed have hatched into females, and no adult males of the species have ever been found.

Since dinosaurs were reptiles, scientists assume they reproduced like reptiles do today. The males may have had simple cloacae or hemipenises or fully developed penises. Some genera of dinosaur may have had one type, others another. Eggs were most likely fertilized inside the female, as this is typical of reptiles. Sometime after fertilization, the female laid her eggs, probably much as a female reptile does

The primitive vertebrates that lived in the Coal Age—long, long before the Mesozoic—reproduced in the water. The fossils of aquatic hatchlings are common in the carbon-rich shales of that age.

today. It is not known how long the eggs were incubated before they hatched. However, it is certain that some dinosaurs—if not all—did not simply bury their eggs in the sand and desert them as many reptiles, like turtles, do today.

Carefully constructed dinosaur nests, along with fossilized eggs, have been found in Montana, France, and Mongolia. The nests were crater-shaped and made of dirt or mud. The eggs found in France are roundish in shape and are thought to have belonged to a dinosaur named Hypselosaurus. Some of the eggs found in Mongolia belonged to Protoceratops and are shaped like a potato. The nests found in Montana belonged to Maiasaura. Hatchlings were found in the nest, along with many pieces of eggshell. Recently, black, pebbled eggshells have also been found in Montana. They may have belonged to Troödon.

The question often arises of how the dinosaurs like the huge sauropods managed to lay eggs without crushing them. One paleontologist has made a discovery of fossilized eggshells that indicates, in his opinion, that the eggs were laid in two long, straight rows. He thinks the eggs were laid while the sauropod mommy was, quite literally, on the move.

It is possible that some female dinosaurs bore their young alive, as do many modern snakes and lizards. Coelophysises have been found with tiny Coelophysis skeletons inside their rib cages. This could be evidence of live birth, but it more likely means that the adults occasionally ate their young.

There is simply no way of answering specific questions about dinosaur reproduction. The primary reason for this is that soft tissue doesn't usually fossilize so scientists can't tell what dinosaurs internal—or external—organs looked like.

There is also no way of knowing the exact logistics of how two dinosaurs—two eighty-ton Brachiosauruses, for instance—managed to copulate. But manage it they did. The genus Brachiosaurus alone survived for some 25 million years.

Q: Just how big were dinosaur eggs?

A: Now this is a thought-provoking question. Let your imagination run wild and you can come up with some mind-numbing possibilities. Think for a minute about Ultrasaurus. It's possible that this dinosaur was a hundred feet (30 m) long and weighed as much as 140 tons (127 t). If that's so, how big would an Ultrasaurus egg have been? As big as a car? As big as a house? Would a one-egg Ultrasaurus omelette feed a whole army?

A bit of quick math tells you that the average chicken egg weighs about 1/30 as much as the chicken. If these proportions hold true for dinosaurs, a 280,000-pound (126,000 kg) Ultrasaurus would lay a 9,333-pound (4,200 kg) egg.

Can you picture a 9,333-pound egg? Of course you can't. A mommy Ultrasaurus couldn't have pictured one either—and she certainly wouldn't have wanted to lay one.

Thank goodness she didn't have to. Dinosaur eggs were, relatively speaking, very small. A medium-sized dinosaur, for instance, laid eggs about the size of a turkey's, or just a bit larger. The largest dinosaur eggs ever found belonged to a ten-ton (9 t) late Cretaceous sauropod called Hypselosaurus. These eggs were only about twelve inches (30 cm) long. An egg that size would have held just under six pints (3.3 l). The shell was a bit more than a tenth of an inch (2.6 mm) thick.

A nest of a Protoceratops—an early relative of Triceratops—was found recently in Mongolia. It contains so many eggs that their total volume is greater than the size of a mama Protoceratops. The only explanation scientists can come up with is to suggest that more than one female used the same nest.

Even the most gigantic sauropods like Ultrasaurus probably didn't have eggs much bigger than this because the bigger an egg is, the thicker the shell has to be to keep it from collapsing. A shell much thicker than that of the Hypselosaurus egg would have posed two insurmountable problems: First, it would have been too thick for oxygen to permeate, so the unhatched babies would not have been able to breathe. Second, the shell would have been so thick and strong that the hatchlings wouldn't have been able to peck their way out.

Scientists estimate that an eighteen-inch-long (45 cm) baby could have curled up comfortably inside a twelve-inch-long (30 cm) egg. If this eighteen-inch baby had to turn himself into a hundred-foot-long Ultrasaurus, he certainly had a lot of growing to do.

Q: Did the mommy and daddy dinosaurs take good care of the baby dinosaurs?

A: What a relief—according to recent scientific discoveries, you can now answer this question with a resounding yes. There is no need for your own little one to have nightmares about little dinosaurs being plunked down unceremoniously on the face of the earth and immediately left to fend for themselves, as is the fate of many of today's reptile babies.

A hadrosaur nest was discovered in Montana in 1978. Eventually, many egg shells and the skeletons of a number of duckbill babies were found. Some of the babies were

Maiasauras may have made nests by first hollowing out the mounds with their powerful hind legs and then shaping them with their forelegs. The mother Maiasaura then probably squatted over the mound, steadied herself with her forelegs, and deposited the eggs. The eggs were laid in two layers—one on top of the other—but no one knows why.

Maiasaura babies were about fourteen inches (36 cm) long when they were born. They seem to have grown to about twice this size while still in the nest.

hatchlings, but others were over three feet (1 m) long, so they must have been at least a few months old. The most fascinating thing about the older babies is that their teeth were worn down, which indicates a degree of parental care: the mother—and possibly the father—was either bringing food to the babies in the nest or taking the babies out to get their own food and then returning with them at night to the safety of the nest.

Many of the volcano-shaped mud nests, which were seven feet (2 m) in diameter and about thirty inches (76 cm) deep, were located near each other. This indicates that the area was actually a kind of dinosaur crèche or nursery. The skull of an adult duckbill was found near one of the nests. The paleontologists who studied the site gave the hadrosaur the name Maiasaura—*maia* means "good mother" in Greek.

The constant presence of adult duckbills would have provided a good deal of protection for the babies. They needed it—they lived right in the middle of Albertosaurus country. There were huge numbers of duckbills in the area, and they probably travelled in herds and roamed long distances from the nurseries to find food. It's possible that the nurseries were watched over by a few adults while the others searched for food. The babies may have stayed in the nurseries until they were old and strong enough to join the herd. Giraffes do this with their young today.

Although all dinosaurs may not have cared for their young so well, there are indications that at least some others did. Families—adult and young dinosaurs together—of Coelophysis and a few other kinds of dinosaurs have been found. Also, a number of sauropod tracks found in Texas indicate that these animals travelled in herds and that the

Although it is possible that Maiasaura males made the nests and took care of the babies, the odds are against it. While males are responsible for nest building and/or child care in some species of fish and birds, it is more common for reptilian mothers to do this work.

young were kept in the middle of the pack. Modern elephants use this technique to protect their young from predators.

Q: Tyrannosaurus was a boy, right?

A: Despite the tireless efforts of many contemporary parents to raise children who are liberated from traditional sex stereotypes, antifeminism rears its monstrous head nowhere more surely than it does in the world of a boy and his dinosaur.

Watch a boy and his friends playing with their toy dinosaurs for a few minutes and you may well discover that Tyrannosaurus rex and all the other "fierce" meat-eaters are all male. The really tough-looking plant-eaters like Stegosaurus and Triceratops are boys, too. If there's a girl dinosaur at all, it will be a hapless Hadrosaurus or slightly dippy-looking Diplodocus.

It is clearly the duty of every fair-minded parent to make sure this male-dinosaur chauvinism doesn't get any worse. If you discover that your son—or daughter—thinks that all the tough dinosaurs were males, point out right away that if there hadn't been mommy Tyrannosaurus rexes, there wouldn't ever have been any baby Tyrannosaurus rexes to grow up into fearsome fifty-foot beasts. You might even try telling your son that some of the girl Tyrannosaurus rexes were twice as tough as some of the boys. He won't believe you, but you will have done your bit to stamp out the sexual stereotyping of dinosaurs.

In case you think I'm exaggerating just how rampant male-dinosaur chauvinism is, listen to this: The other day a friend of mine overheard a couple of boys telling dinosaur stories. The hero of one boy's tale was a Triceratops. This Triceratops—a male—was brave; he was valiant; he was tough. His enemies could bring on the tanks, the planes, the nukes—it didn't matter; this Triceratops couldn't be beaten. All this sounded fine until she heard the line, "And then Triceratops needed reinforcements, so he laid some eggs . . ."

Now really, that's going too far.

"What's this one called, Mommy?"

The most dreaded question of all

Be sure you have this book stuck in your hip pocket—and opened to this particular chapter—whenever you take your child to a museum with a dinosaur display, a toy store with a huge selection of plastic dinosaurs, or one of those animated dinosaur exhibits that are becoming so popular. It's also a handy guide to have on hand at birthday parties or on Christmas morning—anytime your child is likely to get one of those books full of pictures of miscellaneous dinosaurs romping through colorful prehistoric scenes that invariably have no captions—and it's absolutely essential in the event that your child receives one of those currently popular "tubs" full of unnamed dinosaurs.

This unassuming chapter of this unassuming book can finally, at long last, take the dread out of the most dreaded dinosaur question of all: "What's this one called, Daddy? Do you know, Mommy?"

Believe me, not being able to answer this question can have dire consequences. Just imagine the following scenario: It's your four year old's birthday. She has just opened her present from Auntie Jane; it's a big tub of rubber dinosaurs. She grabs one and runs to you. Shrieking with glee, she shoves the hideous, spike-covered blob in your face, smiles sweetly, and—with perfect confidence in your ability to answer—says, "What's this one's name?"

Now you know it's a dinosaur, but that's about all. You start to admit you don't know the name, but the look of confident expectation on your daughter's face breaks you down.

In desperation, you take it from her hand and stare for a moment at its only distinguishing feature, its spikes. You smile back at your daughter and—without flinching—say, "I think it's a Spikeosaurus, honey."

"Oh goody! A Spikeosaurus!" your daughter cries and runs happily away. She is filled with glee. You are filled with guilt.

Images of the future flash through your mind. Your daughter carries her Spikeosaurus with her everywhere; she sleeps with it at night to protect her from monsters. Finally, the time comes when she carries it off with her on the first day of school. You can see the classroom clearly in your mind's eye. Your daughter takes her seat and proudly puts her Spikeosaurus on her desk. Suddenly, the kid next to her says, "Hey, great Hylaeosaurus you've got there."

Your daughter, filled with pity for the other child's ignorance, looks at him and replies kindly, "This isn't a Hy-lay-a-whatever. It's a Spikeosaurus."

The other kid begins to laugh. "SPIKE? SPIKE-o-saurus? There's no such thing!" He grabs your daughter's beloved dinosaur off her desk and holds it high. "Hey," he calls to the other kids. "She thinks this is a SPIKE-o-saurus!" The whole room is snickering now. Pointing. Howling.

It's bad. Oh, it's very bad. But the worst is yet to come: Your daughter will come home that night. And you will have to face her.

Take warning! You just have to know what makes a dinosaur a dinosaur, what makes one dinosaur different from another, and most importantly, how to tell them apart. And this is the place to find out.

Q: What makes a dinosaur a dinosaur?

A: This seemingly innocuous question has a number of variations, including "Why is a dinosaur a dinosaur?", "What is a dinosaur—really?", and "Why is a plesiosaur not a dinosaur?"

Regardless of what the specific question is, the way you answer it is of paramount importance. The patronizing answers we got when we were kids will no longer do. If you try to answer this question with something like "Dinosaurs were big creatures that lived in swamps millions of years ago that died out because they had small brains and were very dumb," you will be greeted with hoots of laughter—probably even from your three year old.

If you try to get away with a facile answer or if you underestimate your child's intelligence for even one nanosecond, you're doomed: You will have goaded her into showing off how much she already knows. She will be forced to strike you down with the Dreaded Dinosaur Inquisition. You'll know it's coming when she smiles sweetly and says, "Gee, Daddy, thanks for telling me that. Since you know so much, I have another question for you: When did Muttaburrasaurus live?" When your face has gone completely blank, she will look upon you with a mixture of love and pity and say, "I'll make it multiple-choice, Dad, so it's easier: a) the Triassic; b) the Jurassic; c) the Upper Cretaceous; or d) the Lower Cretaceous." All the while, you'll know that she already knows what the answer is—it's c) the Upper Cretaceous—but knowing that *she* knows the answer isn't going to help *you*.

A three year old I know recently received a Noah's ark set as a gift. He was horrified when he discovered that no dinosaurs were included among the pairs of animals. He asked his mother how this terrible oversight could have occurred. When she didn't have an answer, he marched to his toy box, got out his dinosaur models, and— with great indignation—placed two of them on the ark. He refuses to play with the ark unless the dinosaurs are included.

Although there's no doubt that kids sometimes have ulterior motives when they ask questions about dinosaurs, they will accept nothing but answers of the highest standard from you. If you don't know an answer, admit it. But run—quicker than a Gallimimus—to this book and look it up.

The question "What makes a dinosaur a dinosaur?" is a critically important one. It is the foundation upon which your entire body of dinosaur knowledge rests. You've simply got to know the answer. And here it is:

There are four characteristics that by definition make a dinosaur a dinosaur. First, they were reptiles. Second, they were land animals. Third, they walked, or ran, efficiently because they had an upright gait; in other words, their legs came straight down from their hips like a dog's or a horse's and did not sprawl out to the side like those of a crocodile or lizard. Fourth, dinosaurs lived only during the Mesozoic, a period of time that began some 225 million years ago and ended about 65 million years ago.

S-o-o-o, as you can see, living in swamps and being big and dumb have absolutely nothing to do with what makes a dinosaur a dinosaur.

Q: Just how many different kinds of dinosaurs were there anyway?

A: It's a little difficult to pin down the exact number of dinosaurs. Dinosaurs are being christened and unchristened at a truly amazing rate. One reliable estimate says that about 340 different dinosaurs have been given names to date. But in their—completely understandable—enthusiasm at making new discoveries, paleontologists have handed out names to nothing more than a tooth or a few bits of bone. Thus, a dinosaur given one name because of a tooth found in Alberta sometimes turns out to be the same as a dinosaur given a completely different name because of a foot found in the outer reaches of Mongolia. Often there is no way to detect these overlaps until a complete—or nearly complete—skeleton of the dinosaur is found.

Sometimes skeletons of dinosaurs are given different names in different parts of the world, and no one discovers the mistake until one paleontologist has the opportunity to study both skeletons. Once the mistake is discovered, the later-discovered dinosaur is unceremoniously unchristened—and then rechristened with the same name as the dinosaur that was discovered first.

Given all these difficulties, one paleontologist estimates that no more than 150 different dinosaurs have been discovered to date. No one knows how many there are for sure, though, and more are being discovered all the time. In fact, around a hundred names have been assigned in just the last twenty years.

This means that unless you have a remarkable bent for science or a photographic memory, you probably won't be able to learn the names of all the dinosaurs, but you *can* learn the names of the twenty or so most common ones, and you should be able to make reasonably intelligent comments about the rest: "Well, I don't actually know the name of this one, but it looks like it's probably a hadrosaur because it has an unusual crest on its head, and most of the dinosaurs that had crests were hadrosaurs." Even the most precocious preschool paleontologist ought to be reasonably impressed with that.

Edward Drinker Cope and Othniel Charles Marsh were two of the United States's most dedicated early dinosaur hunters. They were locked in an extremely bitter rivalry over which of them would make the most important dinosaur discoveries. Spurred on by the feud, the two men described 130 different dinosaur species between 1878 and their deaths in 1897 and 1899, respectively.

Of course, many of these species turned out to be duplicates, but among the many dinosaurs Marsh named were four of the most famous of all time—Diplodocus, Allosaurus, Stegosaurus, and Triceratops—and those found and/or named by Cope included Camarasaurus, Monoclonius, and Coelophysis.

Q: How come dinosaurs have such big names?

A: They just do, that's all. Paleontologists haven't been intentionally inventing names that are impossible to pronounce just to make life miserable for parents. They have simply been following the accepted scientific rules for classifying and naming things. And these rules—believe it or not—are intended to make communication concerning dinosaurs easier, not harder.

When new dinosaurs are discovered they are usually given names that will make it easy for other paleontologists to recognize them. Often they are named after some strange or unique feature or after the place where they were found. Sometimes they are named in honor of some hard-working (and often dead) paleontologist. Many dinosaur names are made out of their Greek roots. Take Triceratops for example: *tri* means three; *cera* means horn; *tops* means face. Then—since you undoubtedly speak Greek—the minute you hear the name you've got the picture. "Right," you say to yourself. "Triceratops, the guy with three horns on his face!"

Two of the most common endings on dinosaur names are *saurus* and *don*. They come from the Greek words for lizard and tooth respectively. Thus, Albertosaurus means "lizard found in Alberta," and Iguanodon refers to the dinosaur with a "tooth like an iguana." The ending *nychus* means claw. Deinonychus, for example, means "terrible claw."

All this makes paleontologists happy. They like Greek. The rules for scientific naming also make it possible for a

Andrew Carnegie has a concert hall <u>and</u> a dinosaur named after him. The multimillionaire financed several expeditions in the western United States between 1895 and 1905. They found many Diplodocus skeletons, and the best of these was named Diplodocus carnegiei.

dinosaur to be called the same thing in every language. Thus, Hypsilophodon, which means "high-crested tooth," is Hypsilophodon in Greek, English, Portuguese, Russian, and Mandarin Chinese. This helps prevent confusion when two paleontologists who speak different languages are talking about dinosaurs. Unfortunately, it's just one more thing that keeps the rest of us confused.

This is particularly true when dinosaurs are named after the obscure places where they are found. Muttaburrasaurus, named after Muttaburra, Australia, is an easy name for the Aborigines from Muttaburra to remember and pronounce, but imagine what it sounds like to the mother of a five-year-old dinomaniac who lives in outer Mongolia. For her, on the other hand, Tuojiangosaurus is a piece of cake. Why, Tuojiang is a spot that's just a ways down the road from her! So take heart. The hardest dinosaur names for you are probably easy for somebody somewhere.

Q: What's your favorite dinosaur, Daddy?

A: Before you say, "Brontosaurus, I guess," stop. This is a trick question of the trickiest kind. Your child knows how you're going to answer this question: you're going to answer it wrong! There is no such thing as a Brontosaurus. Well, there is, but he never should have been called Brontosaurus. His real name is Apatosaurus.

When they first hear about their old friend Brontosaurus, most adults seem to feel as if one of the most precious parts of their childhood has just been taken away. This is a problem

A guide was taking a group of children through a museum one day. When she came to a detailed display that shows a paleontologist at work on a digging site, she said, "Paleontologists find dinosaur bones by digging in the dirt, just like you dig in your sandboxes."

One of the kids brought her back to reality when he piped up and said, with obvious disappointment, "Gee, the only thing I find in my sandbox is cat poop."

Although Megalosaurus holds the honor of being the first dinosaur on record to be discovered and given an official scientific name, an Iguanodon fossil was actually discovered earlier. It is not considered the "first" because it was not scientifically recorded or named until after Megalosaurus.

for those of us who are expected to know things about dinosaurs, but paleontologists have recently—pardon the pun—unearthed a ton of new information, and there's nothing we can do about it.

According to the rules for scientific naming, the first name given to a fossil specimen is the official name. In 1877, an early paleontologist named O. C. Marsh found parts of a dinosaur skeleton in Colorado that he named *Apatosaurus ajax*. In 1879, two of Marsh's collectors found bones in Wyoming that they dubbed *Brontosaurus excelsus*. Unfortunately, both sets of bones belonged to the same animal.

Four years later, things got even more confused. Marsh used the Wyoming fossils to make the first-ever reconstruction of a sauropod—the grouping of dinosaurs to which Brontosaurus belongs. Unfortunately, his reconstruction also included a number of Camarasaurus bones he had found and mistakenly believed were Brontosaurus bones. He also didn't know that his Brontosaurus should have had a long, whiplike tail, and it was years until more accurate renditions of Brontosaurus were made. It didn't matter; this dinosaur was well on his way to fame.

Recently, however, some paleontologists re-examined Marsh's original Apatosaurus bones and discovered that they were, in fact, from the same type of animal as his later-discovered Brontosaurus bones. This means that the name Apatosaurus is the correct one.

A great many people objected to this—after all, Brontosaurus is just about the most famous and well-loved dinosaur of all—but in the end, the paleontologists agreed that the rules of scientific naming had to prevail. (Most paleontologists fear that if they didn't—like boxers—stick to very specific rules, there would be bloodshed, death, and mayhem on digging sites and even in the most sedate museums.) And so it was decided that Brontosaurus—our beloved Thunder Lizard—had thundered for the last time across the pages of history. A creature with a far less imaginative name—Apatosaurus, or the Deceptive Lizard—has taken his place.

Q: How can dinosaurs be so different and still all be dinosaurs?

A: As long as your kid thinks all dinosaurs were gigantic and fierce, she probably won't wonder much about how all the dinosaurs could be in the same family. But as soon as she discovers some dinosaurs were no bigger than chickens and hears the rumor that some of them might have had feathers, she's going to come up with some pretty tough questions. And you want to be ready to answer them, don't you?

Unfortunately, when you begin to read the next few paragraphs you may change your mind. You may decide you don't care one whit about where dinosaurs came from or how they were related. You may even begin to use nefarious tactics to get your child to switch her unflinching love and allegiance from dinosaurs to something comprehensible, like trains.

But I urge you to be brave. Read on. If your child is a dedicated dinophile she is simply not going to switch her allegiance to trains, and you're going to have to learn something about where dinosaurs came from and how they were related. I'll make it as painless as possible, but trust me: you can't have a really good picture of the world of the

Richard Owen, a comparative anatomist who had been greatly influenced by the work of Georges Cuvier, studied Iguanodon, Megalosaurus, and Hylaeosaurus fossils. He realized that these creatures were not simply giant lizards, as had always been believed, and that they deserved their own suborder, for which he coined the word dinosauria *in 1841.*

Owen's concept of dinosaurs as gargantuan reptiles that had once roamed the earth proved irresistible, both to the public and the scientific community, and he was asked to create life-size models of several prehistoric animals for the grounds of the famous Crystal Palace in Sydenham. These models, which we now know contained many inaccuracies, fired the imagination of the world.

dinosaurs without understanding something about their origins and how they are grouped. That means learning something about scientific classification. And the interesting thing about scientific classification is that it helps us understand how different groups of animals evolved and how they are related.

In classifying animals, scientists start with a huge grouping and then break it down further and further. Dinosaurs are members of the kingdom Animalia, which includes all animals, and the phylum Chordata, which includes all vertebrates, or animals with spines. They are members of the class Reptilia—that's reptiles to you and me. The next stage in classification is the subclass; for dinosaurs that's Diapsida, a group of animals that all have two holes in the bony structure of their skulls. (Please keep reading, this gets interesting any second now.) Next comes the superorder; for dinosaurs that's Archosauria. The archosaurs—or Ruling Reptiles—of the Mesozoic included the dinosaurs, the primitive crocodiles, the pterosaurs (the flying reptiles), and a very ancient group of animals called thecodonts.

Thecodonts were very important. They were reptiles that first appeared in the Triassic. Many thecodonts were large, heavy, meat-eating quadrupeds, but some were bipedal. Some were thirty feet (9 m) long; others were about the size of a rabbit. All the other archosaurs—and perhaps even the birds of today—evolved from a common thecodont ancestor.

The thecodonts' most significant characteristic was their ability to vary their gait; they could move with their legs sprawled out to the side like a lizard or raise themselves so they were semierect—like a running crocodile. This was— pardon the pun—a big step forward in evolution; it paved the

A recent discovery in Mongolia may mean that there is a whole new division of dinosaurs in addition to the two long-accepted categories, bird-hipped and lizard-hipped. These dinosaurs have an entirely different kind of pelvis. This type of pelvis is called opisthopubic, *which means "backward pubic bone" in Greek. The dinosaurs are being called segnosaurs after* Segnosaurus, *one of the examples found. They are now being classified as lizard-hipped, but further segnosaur discoveries could radically change our thinking about dinosaurs.*

way for the dinosaurs to develop a fully erect gait, the characteristic that, probably more than any other, gave dinosaurs the evolutionary edge and helped them rule the earth for about 160 million years.

Dinosaurs are further divided into two groupings called orders. These two groups are, unfortunately, not meat-eaters and plant-eaters. That would be too simple. They are Ornithischia and Saurischia. But don't panic. We never need use these two words again. Even the most persnickety paleontologists will allow us to call these two groups, respectively, the bird-hipped and the lizard-hipped dinosaurs.

Unfortunately, there is really no pat way of telling a lizard-hipped dinosaur from a bird-hipped dinosaur, but generally speaking, the swift, two-legged runners, the fierce meat-eaters, and the gigantic, long-necked, small-headed dinosaurs are lizard-hipped dinosaurs; the really strange-looking dinosaurs—the ones with spikes, face-horns, frills, headdresses, or armor—are generally bird-hipped. Most bird-hipped dinosaurs also have an unusual horny, predentary bone—something like a bird's beak—on the front part of their lower jaw, but this isn't exactly something a nonpaleontologist is going to notice.

The lizard-hipped dinosaurs include both meat-eaters and plant-eaters. The bird-hipped dinosaurs seem to have been mostly plant-eaters, but just to confuse things, some may have been omnivores.

Now remember, nobody made up these groupings just to show off how smart they were. The groups are based on real anatomical differences. In other words, all dinosaurs either have bird-type hips or lizard-type hips. This fact tells scientists a great deal about dinosaur evolution. All dinosaurs

The only way to really tell the difference between a bird-hipped and lizard-hipped dinosaur is to examine their pelvis, or hip girdle.

If you examined the pelvis of a lizard-hipped dinosaur, you would find it is made of three main bones, the ilium, the ischium, and the pubis, which are arranged much like those of most lizards. The three bones radiate in different directions. The front bone (or pubis) is pointed forward in most lizard-hipped dinosaurs.

The pelvis of a bird-hipped dinosaur is also made of three main bones, which are arranged much like those of birds. The pubis points backwards and runs parallel to the ischium.

may have evolved from a common thecodont ancestor, but somewhere along the way two different groups emerged and continued to evolve down through the ages into different suborders, families, genera, and species. The Indoor Field Guide to Dinosaurs that follows provides a little more information on these categories and should help you recognize the most common dinosaurs before your child even knows their names.

All this is a fairly simplistic look at the scientific classification of dinosaurs, and I have to warn you that there is some dissension in paleontological circles about which dinosaurs go where. Some paleontologists even want the superorder Archosauria upgraded to a class that includes birds. Others think that dinosaurs should never be considered a single grouping; they say the "bird-hips" and the "lizard-hips" are no more similar to each other than they are to the crocodiles.

So there you have it. It may be about as clear as Mesozoic mud right now, but it should get clearer as you read on.

An Indoor Field Guide to Dinosaurs

Lizard-hipped dinosaurs

The lizard-hipped dinosaurs are divided into two suborders, theropods and sauropodomorphs. They include both the fierce meat-eaters like Tyrannosaurus and the peaceful plant-eaters like Apatosaurus.

Theropods

The word theropod means "beast-footed," which is really a silly misnomer because theropods' feet look a lot more like those of a bird than they do of those of your average beast. In general, the theropods walked on their hind legs and had three clawed, birdlike toes that pointed forward and one that pointed backward. Their arms tended to be short, and their clawed hands were good for grasping.

The theropods were basically meat-eaters, but those with beaks, like Oviraptor, may have been omnivores, eating meat, fruit, or even eggs.

The suborder Theropoda is sometimes broken down into five infraorders. There are two main infraorders: the coelurosaurs, which include speedy bipedal creatures like Coelophysis and Compsognathus, and the carnosaurs, which include fierce meat-eaters like Megalosaurus, Allosaurus, and Tyrannosaurus. Unless your child is really into dinosaurs and you really want to impress him, you might be tempted to skip the other infraorders—the deinonychosaurs, a group of swift, ferocious meat-eaters like Deinonychus and Velociraptor; the ornithomimosaurs like Oviraptor and Struthiomimus; and the miscellaneous theropods like the segnosaurs—but be forewarned that some of these ferocious creatures are starting to become quite popular.

If you are intimidated by all these strange names, don't be. They'll seem like old friends by the time you finish this book—or by the time your child finishes with you!

The word theropod means "beast-footed," but the theropod dinosaurs all had rather birdlike feet. The word sauropod means "lizard-footed," but these dinosaurs had broad, padded feet that were more like an elephant's than a lizard's. Ornithopod means "bird-footed," but the ornithopod dinosaurs, like Iguanodon and Hadrosaurus, certainly didn't have birdlike feet.

Coelurosaurs

Generally, the coelurosaurs were speedy, bipedal creatures like Coelophysis and Compsognathus. Coelurosaurs had delicate builds and hollow bones. Nimble predators, they had long, well-muscled back legs, fairly long arms, small heads, and rather long, flexible necks. They had sharp talons on their hands and sharp teeth. They varied in size from about the size of a chicken to approximately that of an ostrich. The coelurosaurs were probably some of the most intelligent dinosaurs.

As a group, the coelurosaurs were the longest-surviving dinosaurs. They lived throughout most of the Mesozoic, and different types have been found around the world. Some paleontologists think they may have been warm-blooded.

Coelophysis (see-lo-FISE-iss) was one of the early dinosaurs. He was only about three feet (1 m) high at the hips and very lightly built. He was probably a quick runner and voracious eater. Coelophysis's dubious claim to fame is that one has been found with tiny Coelophysis skeletons inside him. While this discovery first flamed the belief that some dinosaurs gave birth to live young, it was finally conceded that Coelophysis was—at least under some circumstances—just your garden-variety cannibal.

Compsognathus (komp-so-NAY-thus) is justly famous as the dinosaur who was no bigger than a chicken and who may have been the smallest adult dinosaur ever. However, the bones of a baby dinosaur named Mussaurus that was no bigger than a thrush have recently been discovered. Compsognathus was a speedy little birdlike predator. Some scientists think she may have been warm-blooded and covered with feathers. Compsognathus lived in the late Jurassic.

Carnosaurs

All carnosaurs were meat-eaters that walked on two legs. They had heavy bones, big heads, strong, thick tails, and stocky, powerful necks. They had pillarlike hind legs, and most had short, comparatively weak front legs. Their razor-sharp teeth were designed for ripping up meat.

Different types of carnosaurs roamed the earth from the late Triassic to the late Cretaceous, culminating in that pinnacle of dinosaur evolution, Tyrannosaurus. Different carnosaur species have been found around the world. There is quite a bit of disagreement on exactly how the carnosaurs should be divided or grouped. Some paleontologists think that carnosaurs were warm-blooded.

Albertosaurus (al-BERT-uh-sawr-us) was a late Cretaceous dinosaur sometimes called Gorgosaurus. Like all carnosaurs, he had a large skull, a strong tail, and daggerlike teeth; he walked on two feet and ate meat. Albertosaurus, although smaller than his relative Tyrannosaurus rex, was still an awesome beast. He weighed about three tons (2.7 t), stood about eleven feet (3.3 m) high, and measured thirty feet (9 m) from nose to tail. His bones were first found in the province of Alberta by Joseph Tyrrell in 1884.

Allosaurus (AL-uh-sawr-us) first lived in the North America of the late Jurassic. Scientists debate—as they do about other carnosaurs—whether she was a swift, vicious predator or a clumsy, lumbering scavenger. She weighed four tons (3.6 t) and stood sixteen and a half feet (5 m) tall. The largest Allosaurus found was forty-five feet (13.5 m) long, but most were about thirty-five feet (10.5 m) long. Allosaurus's jaws were hinged, a bit like those of a snake; she probably swallowed massive chunks of meat whole. She had six-inch (15 cm) claws on her three-fingered hands.

Spinosaurus (SPY-nuh-sawr-us), one of the most unusual carnosaurs, had large spines—some six feet (1.8 m) tall—that probably ran from just behind his head to the top part of his tail. These spines were likely the framework for a kind of "fin" that may have been used as a battle-flag, a sexual signal, and/or a kind of radiator—he may have stood sideways to the sun in the morning to warm his blood. This would have given him a big advantage—if

It was long assumed that the carnosaurs could not swim, but some tracks found in Connecticut indicate that a dinosaur—probably a big, heavy carnosaur—was floating in water and guiding himself along by lightly touching down with his toes. The dinosaur has been named Eubrontes.

both he and his prey were cold-blooded—because his muscles would have been warm while theirs were still cold and sluggish. Later, when the day was hot, he would stand in the shade or face the sun directly and let the breeze carry the excess heat from his body.

Spinosaurus grew to be up to forty feet (12 m) long. He lived during the late Cretaceous. The only Spinosaurus skeleton ever found was in Egypt; unfortunately, it was destroyed during World War II.

Tyrannosaurus rex (tye-RAN-uh-sawr-us) was probably the largest flesh-eater ever to have walked the earth. Her name means "king of the tyrant lizards," and she was the last known carnosaur. She was eighteen and a half feet (5.6 m) tall, fifty feet (15 m) long, and weighed six tons (5.5 t). She had sixty saw-edged teeth, some of which were seven inches (18 cm) long. She had huge jaws; her head alone was four feet (1.3 m) long, and she probably could have swallowed humans whole—if there had been any humans around to swallow.

Deinonychosaurs

This proposed new infraorder would include some of the swiftest and most ferocious dinosaurs, like Deinonychus and Velociraptor; some scientists also include Deinocheirus in this group. Deinonychosaurs' hind legs and heads were specially adapted to making savage attacks. They had huge, razor-sharp claws on their hands and a special sicklelike claw on their feet.

They lived in the Cretaceous and have been found in North America and Asia.

Deinonychus (dyne-ON-ik-us) is considered one of the most extraordinary predators of all time. He was around nine feet (2.7 m) long and about five feet (1.5 m) tall, but he only weighed about as much as a man. This middle Cretaceous theropod's most amazing feature was a five-inch-long (13 cm), sickle-shaped "switchblade" claw on each rear foot. His arms were also unusually long for a theropod, but they happen to have been exactly the right length for

Deinonychus to have held his victim out in front of him while he kicked at its belly and ripped it open with his deadly clawed feet.

Velociraptor (veh-loss-ih-RAP-tor) was somewhat similar to Deinonychus but had a longer, narrower head. She lived in the late Cretaceous.

A complete skeleton of a Velociraptor has been found in Mongolia. She died in a battle to the death with a Proceratops. Her long hands are grasping her enemy's head, and one of her sickle-shaped talons is buried in the Proceratops's belly.

Troödon (TROO-o-don) was a small theropod about whom there has been considerable confusion. It was once believed that he might have been the only known bird-hipped dinosaur that was also a meat-eater, but we now know that he was actually a lizard-hipped dinosaur. Recently, scientists have also discovered that the dinosaur called Stenonychosaurus should have been called Troödon all along.

Stenonychosaurus was considered a deinonychosaur by some paleontologists, but for now, Troödon is not being placed in any particular infraorder. I have put him here only for convenience.

Ornithomimosaurs

This advanced group of extremely active, bipedal dinosaurs looked a lot like ostriches without feathers. They ran on long and thin but powerful hind legs. Their arms were fairly short. They had huge eyes, fairly small heads, and long, slim necks. Their mouths were beaklike and they had no teeth. They included Ornithomimus, Gallimimus, Struthiomimus, and probably Oviraptor.

Different ornithomimosaurs were found from the late Jurassic to the late Cretaceous in North America, Asia, and Africa.

Gallimimus (gall-ih-MY-mus) was probably the largest ornithomimosaur. He may have measured as much as twenty feet (6 m) from the tip of his beaklike mouth to the end of his tail. Some think he may have been the fastest dinosaur. His arms were short, and his hands were not very good for tearing up meat. He may have eaten small animals, but was probably an omnivore.

The largest mounted dinosaur skeleton in the world is a Brachiosaurus, which is in the Humboldt Museum in East Berlin. Some of the fossils were discovered accidentally by an engineer looking for oil in uncharted territory in Tanzania in 1907. A professor from Stuttgart happened to be in the area and came to look at the find. He returned to Germany, raised an expedition, and in 1908 returned to dig up the Brachiosaurus. During the next four years, native porters carried 275 tons (250 t) of fossils from the site on their heads and backs. They had to carry the fossils for forty miles (64 km) through the wilds to reach the East African coastal port of Lindi. From there the bones were shipped back to Europe.

Oviraptor (o-vee-RAP-tor). This dinosaur's name means "egg robber." In the more graphic dinosaur books, Oviraptor is often pictured hovering over a nest with egg yolk dripping from her beak. While she may well have eaten eggs, she had a beak powerful enough to crush bones. Her body was about the size of a turkey's, and she had a long tail.

Miscellaneous Theropods

There are a number of theropods that have not been placed in a particular infraorder yet because so little is known about them. One, Segnosaurus, has recently been given his own infraorder. Not much is known about him, but he was a lightly built meat-eater with a pelvic girdle that is neither bird-hipped nor lizard-hipped.

Sauropodomorphs

The other suborder of lizard-hipped dinosaurs, Sauropodomorpha, includes only two infraorders, the prosauropods and the sauropods.

Prosauropods

The prosauropods seem to have come in a variety of sizes but all had fairly long necks and proportionally small heads in comparison to their bodies. The early prosauropods could walk either on their hind legs or on all fours, but later species were all quadrupedal. They were generally plant-eaters.

Different kinds of prosauropods have been found around the world. They lived during the Triassic and early Jurassic. Some—but not all—paleontologists think that the prosauropods were early ancestors of the sauropods, but regardless, they are related somehow to the sauropods. The only prosauropods your child is likely to care about are good old Plateosaurus and a newly discovered fellow named Mussaurus, who is the proud owner of the smallest dinosaur bones ever found.

Plateosaurus (PLAY-tee-uh-sawr-us) was one of the earlier dinosaurs. One of the only Triassic dinosaurs that is seen much in children's books or toys, he had a long neck and tail and a small head. He was about twenty-six feet (8 m) long. He may have been a forerunner of the huge Jurassic sauropods.

Sauropods

These dinosaurs tend to look a bit like Apatosaurus or Diplodocus: they all have big bodies, long necks, small heads, and whiplike tails. They were huge, four-legged plant-eaters. Their legs were elephantlike, and most had ridiculously small heads compared to their body size. Some probably reared up on their hind legs to reach leaves and twigs on tall trees.

Different types lived from the late Triassic to the late Cretaceous around the world.

Diplodocus's nostrils were located on the top of his head, almost between his eyes.

Apatosaurus (ah-PAT-uh-sawr-us) is probably one of the most beloved of all dinosaurs. Once known to all of us as Brontosaurus, he lost his popular name because of some finicky rules about how scientific names are assigned. He probably weighed about thirty tons (27 t) and was about seventy-five feet (23 m) long. At twenty feet (6 m), his neck was longer than his actual body. His tail was thirty feet (9 m) long. He was only fifteen feet (4.5 m) high at the hips, and his hindquarters were higher than his shoulders, but when he reared up on his hind legs, he was a towering figure. He probably lived in the plains and forests and travelled in herds. He may have been preyed upon by Megalosaurus.

Brachiosaurus (BRAK-ee-uh-sawr-us) was one of the biggest dinosaurs. She lived in the Jurassic. She was eighty-five feet (26 m) long, and she weighed between seventy and eighty tons (63–72 t); that's as much as twenty large elephants. You can tell a model of a Brachiosaurus from models of the other sauropods because her front legs are longer than her back legs; her shoulders were nineteen feet (5.8 m) above the ground, and her head would have been forty feet (12 m) off the ground when she held it up. Although she

probably browsed the leaves on tall trees, some scientists think that she didn't leave her head up for too long—it would have been too hard for the blood to get to her brain.

Diplodocus (dih-PLOD-uh-kus), who was ninety feet (27 m) long, was much slimmer than Apatosaurus or Brachiosaurus; he probably weighed only about twenty-five tons (23 t). Like all sauropods, he was a four-legged plant eater. His powerful, forty-five foot (13.7 m) tail could have been flicked from side to side and used as a powerful whip. Diplodocus probably had the smallest brain—in relation to body size—of any dinosaur.

Supersaurus (SOO-per-sawr-us) is the nickname of a dinosaur known only from a few gigantic bones found in Colorado in 1972. Supersaurus has not yet been officially named or scientifically described. The bones included an eight-foot (2.5 m) shoulder blade, a six-foot-wide (1.8 m) pelvis, and a ten-foot-long (3.1 m) rib. Some paleontologists speculate that Supersaurus may have been ninety feet (27 m) long and could have weighed up to seventy-five tons (68 t). Others think she was even longer and could have weighed up to one hundred tons (90 t). In any case, she must have been huge. One Supersaurus vertebrae was four and a half feet (1.4 m) long!

Ultrasaurus (UL-truh-sawr-us) is the nickname for another dinosaur that has not yet been officially named or scientifically described. This dinosaur's bones were found in 1979 in Colorado, not far from where the Supersaurus bones were found. Like Supersaurus, Ultrasaurus seems to have been built a good deal like Brachiosaurus. Unfortunately, Ultrasaurus is known from only two bones: a five-foot-long (1.5 m) vertebrae and a nine-foot (2.7 m) shoulder blade—the largest dinosaur bone ever found. Some paleontologists think that Ultrasaurus could have been 115 feet (35 m) long and could have weighed 140 tons (127 t). Most other paleontologists make more conservative estimates. Ultrasaurus's shoulder blade is about 25 percent larger than a Brachiosaurus's shoulder blade. If—and it's a big if—these proportions hold true for the rest of the body, Ultrasaurus might have been about one hundred feet (30 m) long, and he might have weighed more than one hundred tons (90 t), but until a complete skeleton is found, no one can really make any acceptable estimates. So far, however, it does look like Ultrasaurus was the biggest dinosaur ever. Unfortunately, he will almost certainly lose the nickname Ultrasaurus when he gets his official scientific name because a recent article in a journal of paleontology points out that the name Ultrasaurus was given quite a while ago to some relatively obscure dinosaur bones. It's also possible that this Ultrasaurus will turn out to be only a species of Brachiosaurus.

Bird-hipped dinosaurs

The bird-hipped dinosaurs were, as far as we know now, all plant-eaters. They are divided into five tidy suborders—no infraorders to worry about here. The suborders are the ankylosaurs, the ceratopsians, the ornithopods, the pachycephalosaurs, and the stegosaurs.

Stegosaurs

The stegosaurs include a number of medium to fairly large plant-eaters. They all had armor, either plates or spikes or both, that ran down the middle of their backs. The only really popular stegosaur is Stegosaurus, although a detailed children's book will sometimes mention Scelidosaurus.

They lived from the early Jurassic to the late Cretaceous and have been found around the world.

Stegosaurus (STEG-uh-sawr-us) lived in the late Jurassic. He is well known—and well loved—for the large, bony plates that ran down his spine and for the four spikes on his tail. His head and brain were very small. He walked on all fours and probably ate low-lying plants since his hips were so high and his shoulders so low.

Stegosaurus is the only plated dinosaur ever found in what is now North America.

An ankylosaur named Euoplocephalus was so well armored that he had bony eyelids!

Ankylosaurs

The ankylosaurs were the plated or armored dinosaurs. They are known as the reptilian tanks of the dinosaur world. Their armor consisted of plates, nodes, knobs, and/or spikes. This armor was generally quite extensive, in contrast to Stegosaurus's plates, which just went down the middle of his back. Ankylosaurs were peaceful plant-eaters. The most popular dinosaurs of this group include Ankylosaurus, Nodosaurus, Hylaeosaurus, and Acanthopholis.

Different ankylosaurs lived from the middle Jurassic to the late Cretaceous in North America, Europe, and Asia.

Ankylosaurus (an-KILE-uh-sawr-us) lived in the late Cretaceous around a lot of heavy-duty dinosaurs like Tyrannosaurus. His bony, spiked plates and his clubbed tail offered him a good deal of protection. He was about twenty-five feet (7.5 m) long, about six feet (1.8 m) wide, and over four feet (1.2 m) tall, and he weighed around five tons (4.5 t). His bones were found in Montana, and he was one of the last dinosaurs to die out.

Hylaeosaurus (hy-LAY-ee-uh-sawr-us) was about fifteen feet (4.5 m) long. Some paleontologists speculate that large spines ran down the middle of her back to just before her hips. This area of her back may have been covered with bone. The spikes may have then continued on down her tail.

Hylaeosaurus lived during the early Cretaceous and was one of the earliest ankylosaurs.

Nodosaurus (no-doe-SAWR-us) was about seventeen feet (5 m) long and six feet (1.8 m) high. His head and body were covered with knobby plates; spikes ran down his sides. He didn't have a club on his tail.

Ceratopsians

The ceratopsians all had large horns protruding from their noses and from above their eyes. They also had large bony frills that ran

Triceratops was about thirty feet (9 m) long, but almost a third of his length was made up of his massive head.

back from their heads and extended over their necks. There are several ceratopsians that make their way into children's books and dinosaur collections, including Protoceratops, Triceratops, Pentaceratops, Chasmosaurus, and Styracosaurus. The beaked dinosaur Psittacosaurus, whose head looks a little like a parrot's, is also a ceratopsian.

The ceratopsians lived from the middle to the late Cretaceous in North America and Asia.

Both male and female ceratopsians had horns, but the youngsters didn't get theirs until they were at least halfway grown.

Chasmosaurus (KAZ-muh-sawr-us) was a long-frilled ceratopsian. He weighed about 2.5 tons (2.3 t) and was about sixteen feet (4.8 m) long. He was only about half as big as Triceratops, but his frill—the bony plate shielding his neck—was proportionally much longer than Triceratops's. He also had two-inch (5 cm) round scales running down his back. He was closely related to Pentaceratops, another long-frilled ceratopsian, who had three brow horns and two protruding cheekbones that looked like extra horns.

Triceratops (try-SAIR-uh-tops) was a short-frilled ceratopsian that lived in the late Cretaceous with Tyrannosaurus. Powerfully built to protect herself, she was twenty-five feet (7.5 m) long, nine and a half feet (2.9 m) tall, and weighed five tons (4.5 t). She was the largest ceratopsian. Her two brow horns were forty inches (102 cm) long, and a third short, thick horn protruded from her nose. She was almost certainly a peace-loving creature unless she was provoked; then she may have charged—horns pointed like lances—hurtling her five tons at speeds of up to twenty miles (35 km) per hour.

Styracosaurus (sty-RAK-uh-sawr-us) was another short-frilled ceratopsian. His name means "spiked lizard," and his most amazing feature was his frill, from which six long, thick, pointed spikes protruded. He also had a twenty-four-inch-long (60 cm) nose horn. He was about six feet (1.8 m) tall and weighed a couple of tons less than Triceratops. He lived in Alberta in the late Cretaceous.

In some duckbill dinosaurs, air passages seem to have run from their nostrils, up through the strange crests on their heads, and down to their throats. A few paleontologists think that this may have allowed them to eat and breathe at the same time. Since they may have had to eat practically without stopping, this would have been a very handy arrangement.

Ornithopods

This is not an easy category for parents. There are at least sixty types of ornithopod dinosaurs, and their physical appearances varied greatly. They walked mainly on their hind legs but may have grazed on all fours. Most had horned beaks rather than teeth at the front of their jaws. There are several families of ornithopods including the iguanodons, the hadrosaurs (like Maiasaura, Hadrosaurus, and Edmontosaurus), the fabrosaurs, and the hypsilophodons.

Different ornithopods lived from the late Triassic to the late Cretaceous, and they have been found around the world.

Edmontosaurus (ed-MON-tuh-sawr-us) lived in what is now the province of Alberta. One of the biggest of the duckbill (or hadrosaur) family, he weighed between three and four tons (2.7–3.6 t) and stretched out to about thirty-two feet (9.8 m). He probably ate tough plants that needed a lot of chewing—he had about a thousand teeth in his mouth! This dinosaur was very abundant in the late Cretaceous.

Hadrosaurus (HAD-ruh-sawr-us) is famous for being the first recorded dinosaur discovery in North America. Although she may have browsed on all fours, most paleontologists believe that she—like other duckbills—walked on two feet with her body held horizontal, the tail balancing out the head. It is no longer believed that duckbills lived in the water, though they may sometimes have taken a quick dive to avoid a hungry Tyrranosaurus rex. Hadrosaurus was somewhat smaller than Edmontosaurus.

Hypsilophodon (hip-sih-LO-fuh-don), with long legs and a slender body, may have been the speediest of the bird-hipped dinosaurs. He probably weighed just a bit more than an average woman. He was only two feet (0.6 m) high and was about five feet (1.5 m) from his nose to the end of his tail. He ran on his two back legs.

Iguanodon (ig-WAN-uh-don) was the second dinosaur to receive a name (Megalosaurus was first) and may have been the first dinosaur ever found. She lived in the early Cretaceous. The largest known Iguanodons were about twenty-five feet (7.5 m) long, about fifteen feet (4.5 m) tall, and weighed about five tons (4.5 t). Her most outstanding characteristic is her sharp, bony thumb-spike; she probably used it to jab enemies in self-defence. The bones of members of the Iguanodon family have been found in every continent but Antarctica.

Lambeosaurus (LAM-be-uh-sawr-us) was another duckbill. He lived in the late Cretaceous. His bones have been found in Alberta and Baja, California. One of the skeletons was forty feet (12 m) long; this makes him the longest known of the ornithiscian (bird-hipped) dinosaurs. Lambeosaurus is also known for his peculiarly shaped head crest, which has been variously described as looking like a hatchet, a flattened-out teakettle, and a peculiar Easter bonnet.

Maiasaura (my-ah-SAWR-uh) was perhaps the most fascinating of the duckbills. *Maia* means, in Greek, "the good mother." She was given this name because her remains were found near a bowl-shaped mud nest with fifteen babies in it. The babies were about a month old. Their teeth were worn down, and this provides evidence that the parents were caring for the young, either by bringing food to the nest or by taking them out to graze and bringing them home. Many nests were found in the area, which suggests that a kind of baby-dinosaur nursery existed. Before this discovery, most paleontologists assumed that all dinosaurs left their hatchlings to fend for themselves, as most reptiles do today.

Pachycephalosaurs

Until recently, the pachycephalosaurs were listed as ornithopods, but now some paleontologists think they deserve a suborder all their own. In general, they have thick, bony plates, or "domes," on top of their heads. Several also had strange bumps, warts, and little horns decorating their noses, faces, or heads. They were bipedal plant-eaters. They had lots of sharp teeth rather than beaks like

In a great catastrophe, a herd of Maiasaura was overwhelmed by an eruption of volcanic ash. The bones are spread over a little less than a square mile (2.6 km^2), and they indicate that there may have been 135,000 dinosaurs in the herd!

most ornithopods. The only pachycephalosaur your child is likely to care much about is Pachycephalosaurus, but Stegoceras (steg-OSS-air-us)—not to be confused with Stegosaurus—is also sometimes mentioned in children's books.

They lived in the Cretaceous and have been found in Madagascar, North America, Asia, and England.

Pachycephalosaurus (pak-ee-SEF-uh-lo-sawr-us) means "dome-headed." Pachycephalosaurus had a nine-inch-thick (23 cm) plate of bone covering his brain. The domes may have been useful for defence or in courtship rituals where the males butted heads like mountain goats when competing for the most-lovely females. This handsome fellow's face and snout were decorated with bony warts, spikes, and knobs, and the back of his skull was covered by lumpy protrusions. Some of his spikes were five inches (13 cm) long. He was about fifteen feet (4.5 m) long.

A group of Triassic reptiles called nothosaurs evolved into land animals and then returned to life in the sea. Some were about ten feet long (3 m). They had long necks, long tails, small heads, and sharp teeth. Their diet was made up of fish and other sea animals. They had webbed hands and feet, along with paddlelike arms and legs. It is quite possible that they came out of the water and moved about on the shore like seals and walruses do today.

Dinosaur Impostors

Dinosaur books and model collections are rife with ignominious impostors—even the cover of this book has one perched on the shoulders of a dinosaur and haughtily flapping its wings.

These great pretenders to the dinosaur throne include—hold onto your socks—Ichthyosaurus, Plesiosaurus, and even Pternanodon, Dimetrodon, and Pterodactylus. It's true. Not one of these creatures was a dinosaur. Dinosaurs, by definition, are Mesozoic land animals who walk with an upright gait. In other words, their legs go straight down from their hips and are tucked under their bodies just like the legs of many animals—elephants, dogs, and horses, for instance—do today. This upright gait was a great evolutionary advantage over the sprawling, crocodile-like gait of many of the dinosaurs' forerunners.

Other nondinosaurs—although I'm sure you already know this—include the woolly mammoths and the saber-toothed tigers. They lived in the early part of our own era, known as the Cenozoic or the Age of Mammals, not in the Age of Dinosaurs at all.

Dimetrodon (dye-MET-ruh-don), a giant lizard-legged creature with a huge fin running from his neck to the beginning of his tail, is often mistaken for a dinosaur. He was really a pelycosaur, one of the ancestors of the mammal-like reptiles. A meat-eater, he was about ten feet (3 m) long.

Dimetrodon lived in the Permian period and had died out by the time dinosaurs came on the scene in the Mesozoic. Dimetrodon seems to have made his way into every dinosaur collection in spite of the fact that he had the sprawling gait of a lizard or crocodile.

Ichthyosaurus (ik-thee-uh-SAWR-us) was a marine reptile that lived in the Mesozoic. Ichthyosaurus was not a land animal; she was built for swimming, with fins and a streamlined head. She ate fish rather than plants and probably gave birth to her young live because she couldn't leave the water to lay eggs. Ichthyosauruses ranged from fifteen to thirty feet (4.5–9 m) long.

Plesiosaurus (PLEE-zee-uh-sawr-us) was a plesiosaur, another group of swimming reptiles. He was an odd-looking creature who was about ten feet (3 m) long. His head was small, his neck long, and his body barrel-shaped. He had paddlelike legs that he probably used to propel himself along near the surface of the water. He lived in the Jurassic, but the plesiosaur group in general was prevalent during Cretaceous times. They ranged in size from eight feet (2.5 m) to forty feet (12 m). They ate fish and sea creatures.

Pteranodon (tair-AN-o-don) was a late Cretaceous pterosaur, a group of flying reptiles; dinosaurs were *land* animals. Pteranodon's body was about the size of a turkey's. She weighed only about thirty-three pounds (15 kg), but her head was a good six feet (1.8 m) long, and her wings spanned twenty-seven feet (8.2 m). She may have been more of a glider than a flier and may have swooped down to get fish. There is some evidence that Pteranodon was covered with light fur, and it seems possible that she was warm-blooded.

Some small pterosaurs were no bigger than sparrows; the largest had wingspans of forty feet (12 m). They may have needed to use thermal updrafts to lift themselves off the ground.

Pterodactylus (tair-uh-DAK-til-us) was a late Jurassic pterosaur. Some species of Pterodactylus were about the size of a sparrow; others were as big as a hawk. Their wingspan was from twelve to thirty inches (30–76 cm). They were tailless, and their legs may not have been much use on land. It's possible that they ate insects.

The whole group of pterodactyls is a suborder of the pterosaurs. They lived in late Jurassic and Cretaceous times. Some may have eaten fish. Pteranodon was actually a pterodactyl, too. The biggest pterodactyl—and probably the biggest flying reptile ever—was named Quetzalcoatlus, after the Aztec serpent god. His wings spanned forty feet (12 m). His small head and long neck measured eight feet (2.5 m). It's possible that he was a scavenger, or he may have even used his long beak to find mollusks in the mud. He lived in the late Cretaceous.

A late Jurassic pterosaur named Rhamphorhynchus was about eighteen inches (46 cm) long, including his tail, and had a wingspan of about four feet (1.2 m). At the end of his long, stiff tail, he had a membrane shaped like a broad, flat leaf. This unusual attachment seems to have been used as a rudder to guide the pterosaur when he was gliding.

Official Classification of Tyrannosaurus rex

	REAL SCIENTIFIC LANGUAGE	MORE ORDINARY LANGUAGE
Kingdom	Animalia	animals
Phylum	Chordata	animals with spines
Class	Reptilia	reptiles
Subclass	Diapsida	diapsids
Superorder	Archosauria	archosaurs
Order	Saurischia	lizard-hipped dinosaurs
Suborder	Theropoda	theropods
Infraorder	Carnosauria	carnosaurs
Family	Tyrannosauridae	tyrannosaurs
Genus	Tyrannosaurus	Tyrannosaurus
Species	rex*	T. rex

* Very few dinosaurs are known—except to paleontologists—by anything other than their genus name. Tyrannosaurus rex is just about the only species name that has become really well known. Thus, we talk about the genus Triceratops, but there are, in fact, different species, like Triceratops alticornis and Triceratops horridus. Thank goodness, nobody cares but the paleontologists.

Adopt a dinosaur!

The good, the bad, and the ugly

A number of worthy environmental organizations have started "Adopt an Endangered Species" programs, which are wonderful because they get people working together to save an animal from that most heinous of all fates, extinction. The only problem is that these programs have come along just a teeny bit late for the dinosaur.

But what the heck. Adopt a dinosaur anyway. It will raise you higher than you ever thought possible in your child's estimation, and it makes a great family project. Just think how much more interesting the world would be if someone had thought of saving the dinosaurs from extinction before they were all extinct!

You do everything just like you would for a normal adopt-an-endangered-species program. Your first step is to pick your dinosaur. You have to decide which dinosaur would be right for you. Be imaginative. No, let me rephrase that—let your imagination run completely wild. Do a little projection and contemplate what it would be like to have a dinosaur for a pet.

If appearance is important to you and your family, consider appearance. Do you want an obviously cute dinosaur or one that's so-homely-he's-cute? Whatever you do, don't forget the old adage that people often grow to look like their pets.

And how about size? The size of the dinosaur you are particularly fond of can do a great deal to enhance—or detract from—your image. Just think how a Tyrannosaurus at the end of the leash could change the impression made by a ninety-pound weakling.

Disposition is another factor. Your dinosaur's overall demeanor will reflect on your character. If, in your political views, you tend to be a dove, you are certainly not going to want to adopt a deinonychosaur. If, on the other hand, you're a hawk, Deinonychus or Deinocheirus might be just the ticket.

The following questions and answers contain a lot of information about dinosaur "superlatives"—in other words, who was the biggest, cutest, meanest, and so on. This should prove invaluable in helping you adopt the dinosaur that's right for you.

Once you've got your dinosaur, you do all the same things that you would for an endangered-but-still-lucky-to-be-around animal. For instance, the whole family can join an organization that's working to save your dinosaur—well, its bones, anyway. Adults can help raise funds and donate money to worthy paleontological societies or museums that have good dinosaur collections. Kids can do classroom projects, draw, write stories, cut out pictures, clip news articles, and build scrapbooks about their adopted dinosaur. Kids also enjoy writing stories about what life would be like if their particular dinosaur were still around. You know the kind of thing: "If my dinosaur, T. rex, were still around, butchers wouldn't hang red meat in their windows anymore . . ."

I have a feeling the adopt-a-dinosaur program is going to be a real hit. So be a trend-setter. Adopt a dinosaur today.

Q: Which dinosaur could we get for a pet?

A: Don't you dare thwart your child's imagination by responding to this question with some mundane answer like, "The dinosaurs are all dead; we couldn't have any dinosaur for a pet." Enter, instead, into the spirit of things and help your little dinomaniac determine exactly which dinosaur would have been most appropriate for a pet—or, better yet, which one would have fit in with your family's particular quirks and idiosyncrasies.

It probably won't take your child long to decide that most of the meat-eaters are right out of the potential pet category. If she doesn't come to this conclusion on her own, just show her pictures of Deinonychus's claws or Allosaurus's serrated teeth.

She might think for a minute that Compsognathus would have made a good pet because he was—not counting his tail—not much bigger than a chicken. But Compsognathus was a carnivore, and he had very sharp, spiky teeth.

A great many of the plant-eaters can be eliminated from the competition due to size alone. Even a young child will be able to figure out that you can't keep a dinosaur for a house-pet if it won't fit into your house.

That leaves us with the medium to small herbivores—well, make that the small herbivores, those that are smaller than a person. Several from this category can be readily eliminated. Lesothosaurus is a cute little bipedal runner that was only about three feet (1 m) long; unfortunately, its teeth were sharp and made for shredding rather than chewing

A fanatical dinosaur fan decided he wanted to have a dinosaur theme for his fifth birthday party. His mother said she would make him a cake shaped like a Stegosaurus and asked what else he wanted to do to carry out the theme.

His mother is quite a good artist and had at one time painted dinosaurs on a couple of his T-shirts. He decided that he would like to have her paint T-shirts like this for each one of the guests. His mother groaned—there were going to be ten kids at the party—but agreed. She spent days working on the shirts. It took even longer than she had expected because her son insisted that she paint a different dinosaur on each shirt.

When she finished, the boy was beside himself with excitement about giving the shirts to his friends. But when the party finally arrived and it was time to hand out the shirts, the boy started to sob, held onto them for dear life, and refused to give them away!

food. If this creature could shred the tough Triassic plants it had to live on, it could shred your furniture, too. Forget it.

Protoceratops, long considered an ancestor of Triceratops, might be in the running. His frill gives him an interesting appearance, and he wouldn't be much higher than your waist. But his face is all beak. And his beak is not only sharp, it's unfriendly looking. Psittacosaurus is another beaked dinosaur, but he has a much cuter face. He kind of reminds me of a parrot. In fact, his name means "parrot lizard." Some artists have painted him purple and gold, and if they are right, he certainly would be an attention-getting pet. He might be considered a little too big, though—about six feet (1.8 m) when standing on his hind legs.

Some of the pachycephalosaurs were fairly small, but with all those knobs and spikes on their faces, they really were ugly. And they had those awful domed heads that they used for butting. Instead of politely scratching at the door when they wanted to go out, they'd probably ram it down.

Your child may just well decide that Hypsilophodon is the winner in the pet competition. He's got an appealing, beaked face. He's a little bit long—six and a half feet (2 m)—but he is bipedal and probably stays fairly horizontal when moving, so he wouldn't seem too huge—not much higher than your hips. Although he was once thought to have lived in trees, that has pretty well been disproven, so you wouldn't have to worry about him hanging from your chandeliers. An extremely fleet-footed creature, he's probably used to running from his enemies and does not seem to be particularly aggressive. Perhaps your child could even saddle him up and ride him. No doubt about it, Hypsilophodon is a good, all-round choice.

Q: Who was the cutest dinosaur?

A: Your child may have such strong opinions on this subject that she will never ask you this question. But if you want my opinion, I can tell you that I cast my vote—unequivocally—for Lambeosaurus. I just can't help myself. I think she is so cute. No one—not even a fan like me—could say she's pretty, but she did cut a dashing picture with that wonderful head ornament of hers, which seems to be shaped like a broken dinner plate, or maybe a flattened-out teapot. If you squint your eyes, it looks for all the world like a soft, round puff of wool on a lamb's head. She even seems—to me—to have a shy, lambish look about the eyes. Whenever I see pictures of Lambeosaurus, I can't help but think how well named she is. One look at her face and I'm imagining fields of gambolling lambs and their woolly mommies.

Well, imagine my consternation when I discovered that Lambeosaurus was named not for her obvious lamblike appearance, but for the great Canadian paleontologist Lawrence Lambe. Some of my friends have tried to convince me that the only reason I ever thought Lambeosaurus looked like a lamb was because of her name, but it's not true. She does look like a lamb. Her name is just a coincidence of cosmic proportions, that's all.

Q: Who was the ugliest dinosaur?

A: There are those who would disagree, but I am convinced that Pachycephalosaurus was the ultimate in ugliness—not just uglier than any other dinosaur, but uglier than

At the height of their glory, the dinosaurs that lived in what is now Alberta's Dinosaur Provincial Park probably dumped, in one year, about 14,245 tons of dung on a square mile of land (5,000 t/km^2).

The ceratopsians, like Triceratops, had bony frills on the back of their necks. Triceratops's frill was relatively short, but one of his cousins, Torosaurus, had a frill that was five and a half feet (1.7 m) wide and eight and a half feet (2.6 m) long—one third of its body length. Torosaurus had the largest head in proportion to its body of any land animal ever known.

any other creature that ever graced the face of the earth. Pachycephalosaurus was very scary looking.

Pachycephalosaurus was one of the domed dinosaurs (domed, not doomed—all dinosaurs were doomed). His skull was covered with a rounded plate of bone that was nine inches (23 cm) thick. Encircling the high, relatively smooth dome were rows of knobs and spikes that looked like giant warts. His forehead looked like it was afflicted with some unmentionable bone disease. And his nose! It was knobbed, warted, and spiked, too.

All those knobs and spikes circling his head made his dome look like some kind of tonsure. Imagine something out of a horror movie based on a punk medieval monk and you've got the picture.

Running a close second to Pachycephalosaurus in the unbeauty contest is Pachyrhinosaurus—a ceratopsian with a short, spiky frill and something that looked like a hollowed-out, sawed-off tree trunk growing on top of his snout. Nobody knows what he did with this "growth," but he probably rivalled Cyrano de Bergerac for being a lonely kind of guy. Maybe he collected rainwater in his stump and let the early feathered theropods use it as a birdbath. I hope so; it would have been a good way for him to make a few friends.

Q: Which dinosaur was the smallest?

A: The smallest dinosaur scientists know much about was Compsognathus, the dinosaur often described in children's books as being no bigger than a chicken. That some dinosaurs were this small is a delight to children, and they love to trick unsuspecting adults into making statements like "All dinosaurs were big," so they can gleefully quote the stats on Compsognathus.

Just so you're prepared, some species of Compsognathus were about four and a half feet (1.4 m) long; others were only about twenty-eight inches (70 cm) long. This is longer than a chicken, but it includes the tail. Regardless, this puts paid to the old idea that all dinosaurs were big.

A couple of other dinosaurs seem to have been even smaller than Compsognathus, but they are known only from sketchy remains. Saltopus seems to have been about twenty-four inches (60 cm) long and about eight inches (20 cm) high at the hips and to have weighed about two pounds (1 kg). This makes him about the size of a cat. He was a swift, sharp-toothed little meat-eater.

The only dinosaur remains smaller than Compsognathus and Saltopus have been baby dinosaurs: a baby Psittacosaurus that was ten inches (25 cm) long and a newly hatched pro-sauropod that was no bigger than a robin—about eight inches (20 cm) long. Found in 1979 in Argentina, it was given the name Mussaurus, which means "mouse lizard," but being a prosauropod, it probably grew to be a lot bigger than a mouse. One paleontologist guesses that it might have grown to be about twenty feet (6 m) long, but nobody will know for sure until a full-grown Mussaurus is found.

Q: Which dinosaur was the biggest?

A: This is one of those questions that can only be answered with umpteen qualifications. The biggest—meaning the tallest

Fossilized bone fragments found in Tanzania suggest that a dinosaur named Tornieria may have been twenty feet (6 m) high at the shoulders. Brachiosaurus, one of the largest known dinosaurs, was about nineteen feet (5.8 m) high at the shoulders. Brachiosaurus's front legs were, of course, much higher than his back legs; Tornieria, on the other hand, had front and back legs of relatively equal length, so he must have been massive indeed.

For now, Tornieria has been classified as one of the titanosaurs, a poorly known group of dinosaurs. The titanosaurs were huge, sometimes armored dinosaurs that were somewhat similar to Diplodocus.

and heaviest—that paleontologists are absolutely sure about is Brachiosaurus, who was forty feet (12 m) tall. He probably weighed well over seventy tons (63 t) and perhaps as much as eighty tons (72 t). There is another fellow that some scientists feel may have tipped the scales at a whopping eighty tons—Antarctosaurus—but he was not as tall as Brachiosaurus.

Dwarfing both of these enormous hulks, however, are a couple of dinosaurs who are still patiently awaiting official names and scientific descriptions. In the meantime, they have been nicknamed Supersaurus and Ultrasaurus. Supersaurus may have weighed somewhere between 75 and 100 tons (68–91 t). Estimates of Ultrasaurus's weight go from 80 tons (72 t) all the way up to 140 tons (127 t). Unfortunately, only a few of these guys' bones have been found so far, but the bones that have been found were big: one of Supersaurus's neck vertebrae was four and a half feet (1.4 m) long, and Ultrasaurus's shoulder blade—the only bone of his ever found—was an amazing nine feet (2.7 m).

Supersaurus is estimated to have been about fifty feet (15 m) tall, and if Ultrasaurus was as big as his supersized scapula suggests, he was probably about fifty-six feet (17 m) tall.

How tall is fifty-six feet? Fifty-six feet means that if you were taking an elevator up to the top of Ultrasaurus's head, you'd have to say, "Fifth floor, please."

Q: Which dinosaur was the longest?

A: Excluding Ultrasaurus—who just might have been one hundred feet (30 m) long—the longest dinosaur was

Diplodocus. Paleontologists know this for sure because they have a complete skeleton, and it shows us that Diplodocus—without even stretching—was a magnificent ninety feet (27 m) long. His neck alone was twenty-six feet (8 m), and his tail was forty-five feet (13.7 m) long. Engineers say he is designed just like a cantilever bridge.

There is another dinosaur who seems to have been just as long as Diplodocus. His name was Barosaurus. He was related to Diplodocus, but he was proportioned differently. His tail was shorter, but his neck was a good four feet (1.2 m) longer. Some scientists think that when Barosaurus raised his head the blood probably stopped flowing to it, so if he used his long neck as a means of getting tasty, tender shoots off the tops of trees, he had to nibble very quickly indeed.

But how long is ninety feet? Dinosaur books are forever telling kids that Diplodocus was longer than two school buses. Do kids really care how long a school bus is? No. They care about important things like how long a Mars Bar is, the relative sizes of different brands of bubble gum, and how many Reese's Pieces make up an inch. So let's describe things in terms that are relevant to kids: It would take, for instance, 270 Mars Bars to make a line from Diplodocus's nose to the tip of his tail, so if a kid ate a Mars Bar a day, it would take him most of a school year to eat his way along Diplodocus. If he balanced Double Bubble all along Diplodocus's spine and started to chomp away, it would take him two years—at the rate of three Double Bubbles a day—to chew his way from one end to the other. And Reese's Pieces? Well, ET himself would have been sick of them before he finished eating the 4,320 Reese's Pieces it would take to go the length of a Diplodocus.

Now *that's* relevant.

Mamenchisaurus, a relative of Diplodocus found in Mongolia, had the longest neck of any dinosaur ever known. Mamenchisaurus's entire length may have been more than about eighty-six feet (27 m)—and his neck made up thirty feet (9 m) of it! His neck contained nineteen vertebrae, some of which were five feet (1.5 m) long.

Dinosaur Superlatives

Before you and your child make a final decision about which dinosaur you're going to adopt, your child will probably want to know all kinds of things about which dinosaurs were the "most" or the "best"—the real champions in any particular category. Unfortunately, it's almost impossible to guess what kind of categories your exceedingly imaginative little nipper is going to come up with. The following represent, at least, some of the possibilities.

Before you read on, however, a word of caution: there is disagreement among paleontologists on these figures, and many of the figures are estimates. We can't know, for instance, exactly how much a dinosaur weighed because we don't have a dinosaur around to weigh.

Longest dinosaurs: Barosaurus and Diplodocus

Both were about 90 feet (27 m) long. It is possible, however, that the dinosaurs now nicknamed Supersaurus and Ultrasaurus will prove to be longer when more is discovered about them. These two now have estimated lengths of 80 to 100 feet (24–30 m) and 100 to 115 feet (30–35 m) respectively.

Heaviest dinosaurs: Brachiosaurus and Antarctosaurus

Both have been estimated to weigh between seventy and eighty tons (63–72 t), but Antarctosaurus may have been the slimmer of the two. It is possible that Supersaurus and Ultrasaurus were even heavier, but no one knows yet.

Widest dinosaur: Ankylosaurus

One of the "reptilian tanks" of the dinosaur world, Ankylosaurus was sixteen feet (5 m) wide, although he wasn't much more than thirty-two feet (10 m) long.

A fellow I know who is six feet, eleven inches tall took his son to a museum one day to look at the dinosaur bones. The museum had an Apatosaurus femur mounted so that children could reach up and touch it. The child asked what it was, and the father explained that it was a dinosaur's thigh bone. The boy looked at the bone, then looked at his father and said, "Gee, Dad, I guess you're not too tall after all."

Smallest dinosaur: Some species of Compsognathus

Some of these dinosaurs have been measured at only twenty-eight inches (70 cm) long, and that's including the tail! It is possible that a Saltopus adult was only about twenty-four inches (60 cm) long, but we don't have as much information about Saltopus as we do about Compsognathus.

Earliest-known dinosaur: Staurikosaurus

The earliest-known dinosaur is a bipedal carnivore named Staurikosaurus, who may have lived as early as the middle Triassic. She was about five feet (1.5 m) long and may have weighed about sixty-six pounds (30 kg). The skeleton, which was found in Brazil, does not clearly indicate whether Staurikosaurus was a bird-hipped or a lizard-hipped dinosaur, and some scientists say this indicates that both types of dinosaurs evolved from a common ancestor.

The earliest-known bird-hipped dinosaur was called Pisanosaurus. It was a plant-eating biped that was only about three and a half feet (1 m) long.

Smartest dinosaur: Troödon (formerly known as Stenonychosaurus)

Troödon seems to have had the largest brain of any dinosaur in relation to his body size. This probably indicates that he was the smartest fellow around. Some scientists think he was as smart as an ostrich, and that's smarter than any reptile on earth now.

Dinosaur with the smallest brain in relation to body size: Probably Diplodocus

Diplodocus probably weighed about twenty-five tons (23 t), but her brain probably weighed only a few ounces! Still, we should refrain from making the pronouncement that Diplodocus was the dumbest dinosaur.

It is supposed that Troödon had the best eyesight of any dinosaur. His eyes were very large for his body size, and they were spaced well apart, which means he could probably judge distances well. They were also directed forward, just like our eyes.

Many dinosaurs had keen senses. Natural casts formed of dinosaur brains show scientists that some dinosaurs had a very acute sense of smell. There is evidence that others, like the sauropods and hadrosaurs, may have had very good hearing.

Fastest dinosaur: Gallimimus or Troödon

Scientists have estimated the speed of these two dinosaurs at thirty-five miles (56 km) per hour and fifty miles (80 km) per hour respectively, but nobody knows exactly how fast these or any other dinosaurs could run.

Most famous dinosaur that wasn't a dinosaur: Pteranodon

This creature was a flying Mesozoic reptile and not a dinosaur at all.

Most beloved dinosaur: Apatosaurus

If you could get kids everywhere to vote on the dinosaur they love best, Apatosaurus—the old Brontosaurus—would almost certainly win, but Triceratops, Stegosaurus, and Iguanodon would be in the running too.

Most all-round popular dinosaur: Tie between Triceratops and Iguanodon

If you take lovableness out of the question, these two dinosaurs would probably even triumph over Apatosaurus in a vote.

Most respected dinosaur: Tyrannosaurus rex

T. rex is certainly thought of as the epitome of ferociousness and strength by children everywhere, but while he is the most respected, that doesn't mean that he is the most beloved.

Dinosaur most likely to bring on nightmares: Tie between Deinocheirus and Deinonychus

Deinocheirus's arms were nine feet (3 m) long with eight- to twelve-inch-long (20–30 cm), sharp, hooked claws. Deinonychus was much

Gideon Algernon Mantell, a medical doctor and amateur paleontologist, described Iguanodon in 1822 and named him in 1825, but he credits his wife with actually finding the first Iguanodon fossils—a number of teeth she found in some gravel in Sussex, England.

Mantell traced the gravel in which the teeth were found to its original source, one of the quarries in the Tilgate forest region. He diligently searched the quarries, and with the help of alert quarrymen, discovered more Iguanodon fossils.

In 1933, Mantell also described Hylaeosaurus.

smaller. Her razor-sharp claws were only five inches (13 cm) long, but we know for sure that she used them to disembowel her struggling prey.

Dinosaur with the most fearsome head: Styracosaurus

A few dinosaurs are in the running for this award, but Styracosaurus, the Spiked Lizard, would probably win. He was a short-frilled ceratopsian, but extending from around the rim of his frill were six huge, tusklike spikes. The spikes were sharp, pointed, and about twenty-four inches (60 cm) long. He also had a nose horn of about the same length and two small horns over his eyes.

Scariest flying creature: Quetzalcoatlus

Although the pterodactyl Quetzalcoatlus, with its wing span of forty feet (12 m), was the largest flying creature ever known, some early pterodactyls were no bigger than a sparrow.

Most misunderstood dinosaur: Triceratops

This dinosaur's huge, sharp horns make him look mean and fierce, but he was probably a very peaceful fellow who only used his horns when terribly provoked.

Dinosaur with the most imaginative means of protection: Euoplocephalus

Euoplocephalus probably could have felled a tyrannosaur four times her size with one solid whack of the boulderlike club at the end of her swinging tail. Ankylosaurus had a tail club too.

Strangest-looking dinosaur: Pachycephalosaurus

With a nine-inch-thick (23 cm) plate on his domed skull, wartlike spikes and bumps circling the dome, and bony spikes on his nose,

Pteranodon may have used the long tubular crest that extended from the back of his head as a rudder when flying, or perhaps as a kind of brake to help him stop when he was landing.

Pachycephalosaurus was a pretty strange-looking dinosaur, but the hadrosaur Parasaurolophus—the dinosaur with the 3.3-foot (1 m) tube running back off the top of her head—runs a close second.

Most all-round unusual dinosaur: Spinosaurus

This dinosaur had a row of six-foot-high (1.8 m) spines running down the middle of his back. They probably supported a huge sail or fin that helped him control his body temperature. A couple of other dinosaurs had spines on their backs, but their spines were not nearly so high. The creature famous for the sail on her back, Dimetrodon, was a reptile from the Permian period who had died out long before the dinosaurs came on the scene.

Best mommy dinosaur: Maiasaura

Although other dinosaurs may have cared for their young well, many scientists are sure Maiasaura was a good mother. She laid her eggs extremely carefully in layers, covering each layer with sand before she went on to the next. Each layer of eggs was set out in a pattern shaped like the spokes of a wheel. The whole nest was then covered with sand to keep it warm. Fossils found near these nests indicate that the youngsters stayed around for some time, presumably being cared for by their mothers.

Bibliography

Digging Dinosaurs by John R. Horner, Workman Press, New York, 1989.

The Dinosaur Encyclopedia by Dr. Michael Benton, Julian Messner, New York, 1984.

The Dinosaur Heresies by Dr. Robert T. Bakker, Morrow, New York, 1986.

The Dinosaurs of North America (juvenile) by Helen Roney Sattler, Lothrop, Lee and Shepard Books, New York, 1981.

Discovering Dinosaurs (juvenile) by Victoria Crenson, Price, Stern, Sloan, Inc., Los Angeles, 1988.

A Field Guide to Dinosaurs by David Lambert, Avon Books, New York, 1983.

The Great Dinosaur Hunters and Their Discoveries by Edwin H. Colbert, Dover Publications, New York, 1984.

The Illustrated Dinosaur Dictionary by Helen Roney Sattler, Lothrop, Lee and Shepard Books, New York, 1983.

The Illustrated Encyclopedia of Dinosaurs by Dr. David Norman, Crescent Books, New York, 1983.

The New Dinosaur Dictionary by Donald F. Glut, Citadel Press, Secaucus, New Jersey, 1982.

A New Look at Dinosaurs by Dr. Alan Charig, Heinemann, London, England, 1979.

An Odyssey in Time: The Dinosaurs of North America by Dr. Dale Russell, University of Toronto Press, Toronto, 1989.

The Riddle of the Dinosaurs by John Noble Wilford, Alfred A. Knopf, New York, 1986.

The Successful Dragons: A Natural History of Extinct Reptiles by Dr. Chris McGowan, Samuel Stevens, Toronto and Sarasota, 1983.

When Dinosaurs Ruled the Earth (juvenile) by Dr. David Norman, Marshall Cavendish Ltd., London, England, 1985.

Teri Degler was raised in Idaho, but has lived in Toronto, where she works as a writer and editor, since 1974. She has an MA in special education and has done extensive work with young people setting a base for her first book, recently expanded and published as *Love, Limits, and Consequences: A Positive, Practical Approach to Kids and Discipline*.

     With the publication of her very successful books *Scuttlebutt . . . And Other Expressions of Nautical Origin* and the companion volume *Straight from the Horse's Mouth . . . And Other Animal Expressions*, Teri has become a popular Canadian author.